· SCHOLASTIC SUCCESS WITH ·

TODDLER
WORKBOOK

SCHOLASTIC
Teacher
RESOURCES

Editor: Liza Charlesworth
Cover design by Tannaz Fassihi; cover art by Rob McClurkan
Interior design by Mina Chen
Interior illustrations by Doug Jones (3, 6-9, 47-72, 163-167, 169-179, 202, 204, 224, 226, 248, 250-255, 259-284, 367, 369, 371, 373, 375, 379, 392); Jannie Ho (109-148); John Lund (205, 221-223, 225, 399); Fhiona Galloway (383, 401, 415)
All other images © Shutterstock.com

ISBN 978-1-338-83643-1
Scholastic Inc., 557 Broadway, New York, NY 10012
Copyright © 2022 Scholastic Inc.
All rights reserved. Printed in USA.

1 2 3 4 5   144   26 25 24 23 22

"Nothing succeeds like success."

Alexandre Dumas the Elder, 1854

Dear Parents:

Congratulations! Your child is a toddler. Toddlers are exuberant, creative, playful, and curious. That means they are ready to learn. Inside this colorful workbook, you'll find a treasure trove of engaging, skill-building activities developed especially for toddlers. Topic areas include:

★ **Fine Motor Skills**   ★ **Colors**   ★ **Matching**

★ **Tracing**   ★ **Shapes**   ★ **Sorting**

★ **Alphabet**   ★ **Cutting & Pasting** ★ **Easy Rhymes**

★ **Numbers**   ★ **Basic Concepts**   ★ **Easy Songs**

We provided two sections related to each topic—the second slightly more challenging than the first—to ensure your toddler gets plenty of practice. We've also included a bonus "All About Me" section that you and your child can work on together to celebrate the things that make him or her unique. In addition, you'll find 24 big, two-sided flash cards, PLUS 24 bright stickers!

So, turn the page and get started today. This workbook, created by educational experts at Scholastic, will help set your toddler on a path to a lifetime of exciting learning.

Enjoy!

The Editors

Learn and Grow With the Toddler Workbook!

Your child's toddler years represent an exciting opportunity to acquire important skills. This workbook has been carefully designed to help ensure your child attains the tools he or she needs to maximize learning now, in your home, and later, at school and in the world at large. On the pages that follow, you'll find 400+ age-perfect activities in 12 foundational areas.

Fine Motor
- Introduction to Writing/Drawing
- Easy Writing
- Easy Drawing
- Extended Practice

Colors
- Introduction to Colors
- Identifying Colors
- Coloring
- Extended Practice

Matching
- Introduction to Matching
- One-to-One Correspondence
- Fine Motor Skills
- Extended Practice

Tracing
- Introduction to Tracing
- Lines and Patterns
- Shapes
- Extended Practice

Shapes
- Introduction to Shapes
- Identifying Shapes
- Coloring
- Extended Practice

Sorting
- Introduction to Sorting
- Simple Grouping
- Fine Motor Skills
- Extended Practice

Alphabet
- Introduction to A–Z
- Letter Formation
- Initial Letter Sounds
- Extended Practice

Cutting & Pasting
- Introduction to Cutting & Pasting
- Cutting Shapes
- Pasting Shapes
- Extended Practice

Easy Rhymes
- Introduction to Easy Rhymes
- Listening & Speaking
- Following Directions
- Fine Motor Skills

Numbers
- Introduction to 1–10
- Number Formation
- Counting
- Extended Practice

Basic Concepts
- Introduction to Basic Concepts
- Opposites
- Coloring
- Extended Practice

Easy Songs
- Introduction to Easy Songs
- Listening & Singing
- Following Directions
- Fine Motor Skills

About This Workbook

No doubt, your spirited toddler keeps you quite busy. For that reason, we've made this workbook VERY simple to use. Each activity page requires just a few supplies (see page 10) and absolutely no prep. Here's a quick tour of an activity page:

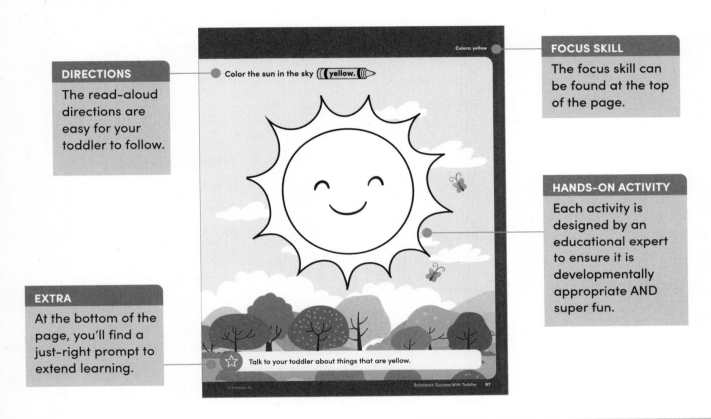

DIRECTIONS
The read-aloud directions are easy for your toddler to follow.

EXTRA
At the bottom of the page, you'll find a just-right prompt to extend learning.

FOCUS SKILL
The focus skill can be found at the top of the page.

HANDS-ON ACTIVITY
Each activity is designed by an educational expert to ensure it is developmentally appropriate AND super fun.

Within the activity page image:
Colors: yellow
Color the sun in the sky yellow.
Talk to your toddler about things that are yellow.
Scholastic Success With Toddler 87

But wait. There's more. This very special workbook also includes...

ALL ABOUT ME BOOKLET
Celebrate your toddler's passions and milestones by working together to complete this very special booklet you both will treasure for a lifetime!

FLASH CARDS & STICKERS
In the back of this workbook, you'll find 24 big, two-sided flash cards to boost your toddler's vocabulary skills, PLUS 24 colorful stickers to reward learning.

For tips on making this workbook an enjoyable, learning-rich experience, turn to page 10.

TABLE OF CONTENTS

SHAPES

CUTTING & PASTING

BASIC CONCEPTS

MATCHING

SORTING

EASY RHYMES

MORE FINE MOTOR SKILLS

MORE TRACING

MORE ALPHABET

MORE NUMBERS

MORE COLORS

Tips to Maximize Learning and Joy!

Welcome to the *Scholastic Success With Toddler Workbook*. Here are some quick ideas to ensure your child's learning experience is stress-free, safe, and fun.

SIMPLE SUPPLIES

It's wise to gather the necessary tools your toddler will need BEFORE the learning journey begins. Don't worry, we've kept things VERY simple.

Nontoxic Crayons: To complete the workbook pages, these 11 colors are required: red, blue, yellow, green, orange, pink, purple, brown, white, black, gray. Consider purchasing jumbo-size or special toddler-grip crayons to accommodate your little learner's small hands and developing fine motor skills. (Washable markers can also be used but will require close supervision.)

Safety Scissors: The cut-and-paste section of the workbook requires a pair of small safety scissors. We suggest plastic ones, which are available at most office supply stores. **Always supervise children when using scissors.**

Nontoxic Glue Stick: Your child will also need a glue stick. A large-size glue stick is suggested, as it is easy for small hands to grip and manipulate.

TIP: We suggest you keep these tools in a plastic bin stored beside the workbook. That way, your toddler will be able to sit down and learn—in an instant!

LEARNING SESSIONS

⭐ **Invite your toddler to dip into this workbook a few times a week—or more—but be sure to keep it a joyful experience.** Turn to the pages when he or she is alert, focused, and ready to learn. If your child is frustrated or cranky, go to the park or take a book break and read a toddler-perfect title. We've included a list of our favorites on page 12.

⭐ **Choose a quiet, comfy, clutter-free location to learn.** A tabletop or the floor are great options. Make sure you can see and supervise your child at all times.

⭐ **Read the directions aloud to your toddler, then complete the pages together.** At first, children will need a lot of guidance and help from you. That said, as they grow accustomed to the activities, they will likely be able to complete many of the pages independently.

⭐ **Set reasonable expectations for your toddler.** For example, your child may color wildly outside the lines, have a hard time tracing a number 2, or need your steady hand to help cut and paste a square. No worries! It is a triumph for young children to sit, focus, and simply *try*. It is also a triumph for them to enjoy acquiring new skills. Feeling free to take risks and make mistakes is a big part of the early learning process. If your toddler colors a frog purple instead of green, applaud his or her effort. Why? Every time children use a crayon, they learn about colors. Every time children point to a letter *M*, they develop alphabet skills. Every time children trace a heart or cut out a circle, they build important fine motor skills.

⭐ **Remember, each child gains mastery at a different pace.** Toddlers are at the very beginning of their educational journey. They will have many years to hone their coloring, writing, counting, reading, and cutting skills. So, relax and enjoy. The most important thing is that your child feels good about trying new things. For that reason, it's a great idea to follow up a learning session with a happy thumbs-up or a reward sticker. Sending the message that attaining knowledge is an enjoyable experience is one of the greatest gifts you can give your toddler.

SAFETY FIRST!

TODDLERS ARE INQUISITIVE AND CURIOUS. That makes them prone to put things in their mouths, such as crayons or glue sticks. In addition, they lack fine motor skills, which can make even safety scissors slightly hazardous. For that reason, make sure to explain and model the safe use of these items. And if your toddler is too young to understand, simply put the workbook and tools away for a few months until he or she is ready to use them.

MOST IMPORTANT, MAKE SURE TO NEVER LEAVE YOUR TODDLER UNSUPERVISED—EVEN WITH A WORKBOOK AND CRAYONS. TODDLERS ARE UNPREDICTABLE, AND THEIR SAFETY SHOULD ALWAYS BE YOUR FIRST PRIORITY.

Toddler Book Breaks

Looking for some rollicking read-alouds for young children? Choose books with simple plots, playful language, and colorful illustrations or photos. Here are a few of our very favorite titles.

Clifford the Big Red Dog
by Norman Bridwell
(Scholastic)

You Are My Sunshine
by Jimmie Davis and Caroline Jayne Church
(Scholastic)

Bye-Bye, Train
by Pamela Chanko
(Scholastic)

Little Heroes of Color
by David Heredia
(Scholastic)

My Tickle Toes
by Carolina Búzio
(Scholastic)

Peppa Pig: Learning to Share
By Meredith Rusu
(Scholastic)

Silly Monsters at Mealtime
by Kerilyn Acer
(Scholastic)

I Spy Letters
by Jean Marzollo
(Scholastic)

No, David!
by David Shannon
(Scholastic)

MORE FAVORITES

My Heart Fills With Happiness
by Monique Gray Smith
(Orca Book Publishers)

The Pout-Pout Fish
by Deborah Diesen
(Farrar, Straus and Giroux)

Goodnight, Goodnight Construction Site
by Sherri Duskey Rinker
(Chronicle Books)

Whose Toes Are Those?
by Jabari Asim **(LB Kids)**

Dragons Love Tacos
by Adam Rubin **(Dial Books)**

Crankenstein
by Samantha Berger **(Little, Brown)**

Don't Let the Pigeon Drive the Bus
by Mo Willems **(Hyperion Books)**

The Day the Crayons Quit
by Drew Daywalt **(Philomel Books)**

I Will Be Fierce!
by Bea Birdsong **(Macmillan)**

Hop on Pop
by Dr. Seuss **(Random House)**

Bear Snores On
by Karma Wilson **(Little Simon)**

On the Night You Were Born
by Nancy Tillman
(Feiwel & Friends)

Baby Says "Moo!"
by JoAnn Early Macken **(Little, Brown)**

Drawn Together
by Minh Lê **(Little, Brown)**

Blue Hat, Green Hat
by Sandra Boynton **(Little Simon)**

FINE MOTOR SKILLS

★ This section will help your toddler develop fine motor skills. Read the directions aloud. Then demonstrate how to draw spaghetti, swirls, spots, stripes, and more.

★ Remember, toddlers are just learning how to use crayons, so don't worry if their attempts at straight stripes look more like wiggly worms. The important thing is to promote practice and boost confidence.

★ Follow up the session with the starred EXTRA activity at the bottom of the page. This will help build your toddler's listening and speaking skills.

★ To reinforce learning, provide blank paper. Then invite your toddler to scribble and/or draw whatever he or she likes. Proudly display his or her creations on a festive bulletin board or your refrigerator.

SUPPLIES: crayons or washable markers

Draw more spaghetti in Monster's bowl.

 Talk with your toddler about silly things a monster might eat.

Draw more stripes on the zebra.

 Talk to your toddler about zebras. What two colors are they?

Draw more swirls on Lion's lollipop.

 Talk to your toddler about lions. Can he/she roar like a lion?

Draw more spots on the dinosaur.

 Talk to your toddler about dinosaurs. Can he/she walk like a big dinosaur?

Draw more cat food in the bowl.

 Talk to your toddler about cats. Can he/she meow like a cat?

Draw more wiggly worms in the pond.

⭐ **Talk to your toddler about worms. Can he/she wiggle like a worm?**

Bubbles, bubbles! Draw more bubbles.

 Talk to your toddler about bubbles. What shape are they?

Draw more tentacles on the jellyfish.

 Talk to your toddler about jellyfish. Where do they live?

Draw more rays on the happy sun.

 Talk to your toddler about the sun. Is it hot or cold?

·SCHOLASTIC SUCCESS WITH·

TRACING

★ This section will introduce your toddler to tracing. Read the directions aloud. Then demonstrate how to trace waves, lines, wheels, balloons, and more.

★ If your toddler struggles to trace the dashed images, feel free to guide his or her hand.

★ Follow up the session with the starred EXTRA activity at the bottom of the page. This will help build your toddler's listening and speaking skills.

★ To reinforce learning, use a pencil to draw simple dashed-line drawings on paper. Then challenge your toddler to trace over them with crayons or markers.

SUPPLIES: crayons or washable markers

Trace the waves in the ocean.

 Talk with your toddler about things that live in the ocean.

Trace the snail trails.

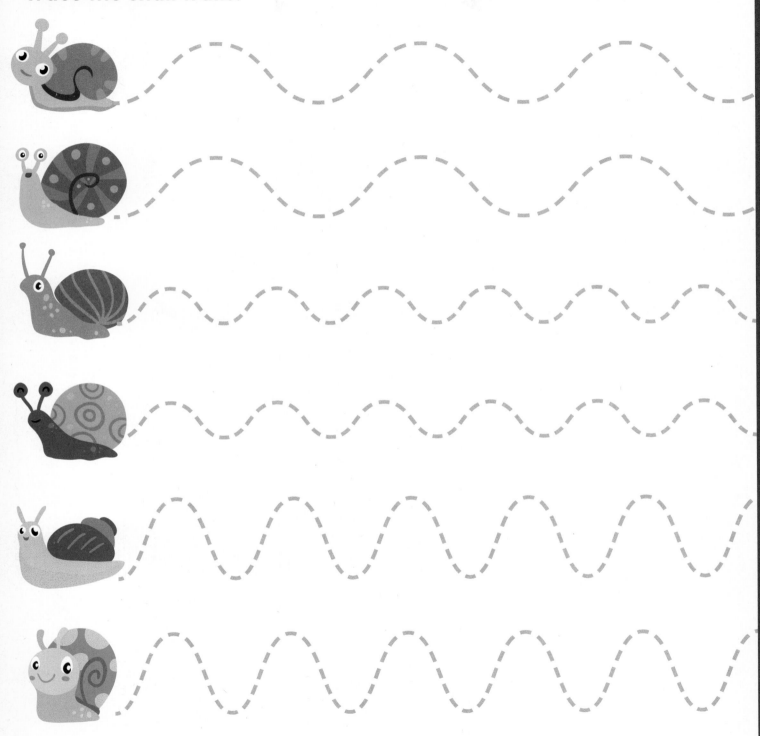

 Snails are small. What other animals are small?

Trace the flower stems.

 Talk about flowers. Ask your toddler what animals he/she sees in this garden.

Trace the lollipop sticks.

 Talk about treats. Discuss your toddler's favorite treats.

Trace the lines on the baby's blanket.

 The baby is sleeping. Invite your toddler to say, "Shhhhhhhh."

Trace the top of the caterpillars.

 What do caterpillars turn into? Talk about it with your toddler.

Trace the sails on the sailboats.

 Do sailboats travel on land or water? Talk about it with your toddler.

Trace the wheels on the cars.

 Talk to your toddler about cars. What other things have wheels?

Trace the pizza slices.

 Invite your toddler to tell you the shape of the pizza slices.

Trace the faces.

 Can your toddler find the happy face?
The sad face? The surprised face?

Trace the top of the tall buildings.

 Has your toddler ever been in a tall building? Talk about it.

Trace the bear's balloons.

 Invite your toddler to tell you the shape of the bear's balloons.

Trace the books.

 Invite your toddler to tell you what vehicle he/she sees on each book.

Trace the windows and door of the house.

 Invite your toddler to tell you the shape of the house's windows and door.

Trace the flags.

 Invite your toddler to tell you the shape of the flags and what is on each.

Trace the signs.

 Invite your toddler to tell you what animals he/she sees on each sign.

Trace the cookies.

 Invite your toddler to tell you the shape of the cookies.

Trace the kites in the sky.

Where do kites fly? Talk about it.

Trace the presents.

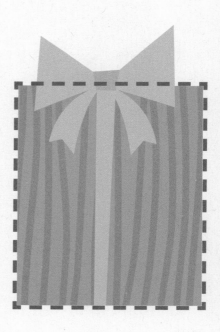

 Invite your toddler to imagine what might be inside each gift box.

Trace the stars in the sky.

 Talk about the stars. Do we see them during the day or at night?

Trace the bananas on the table.

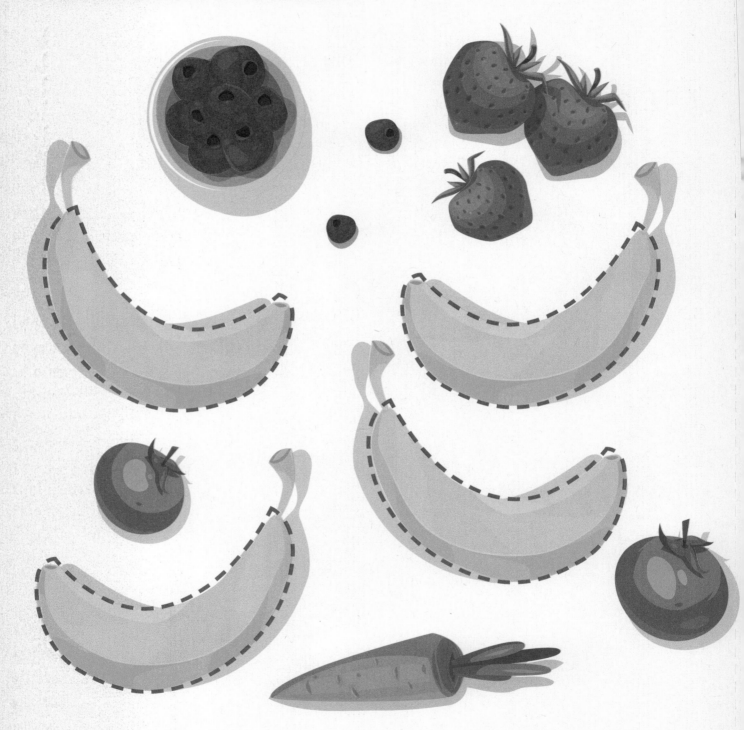

 Invite your toddler to tell you his/her favorite fruit.

Trace the lines on the rainbow.

 Point to each rainbow color and say its name. Then invite your toddler to say the names with you.

SCHOLASTIC SUCCESS WITH

ALPHABET

★ This section will introduce your toddler to the alphabet. Read the directions aloud. Then invite him or her to trace the featured letter, such as *A*.

★ Point to the two items that begin with the featured letter, such as *apple* and *ant*. Read them aloud slowly and clearly several times. Then invite your toddler to chime in and/or identify these items.

★ Follow up the session with the starred EXTRA activity at the bottom of the page. This will help build your toddler's listening and speaking skills.

★ To reinforce learning, point out the featured letter when you spot it in books, product boxes, or signs. Or, challenge your toddler to find the letter by saying, "I spy a/an *(letter)* on this *(item)*. Can you find it?"

SUPPLIES: crayons or washable markers

Trace the letter A. Then color it.

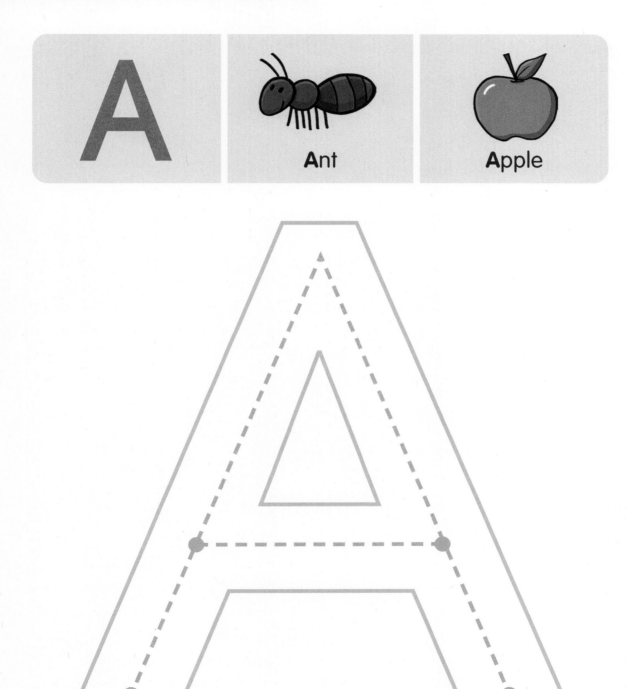

Ant

Apple

 Talk with your toddler about things that begin with the letter A.

Trace the letter B. Then color it.

 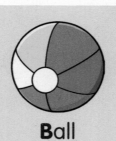 **B**all  **B**ear

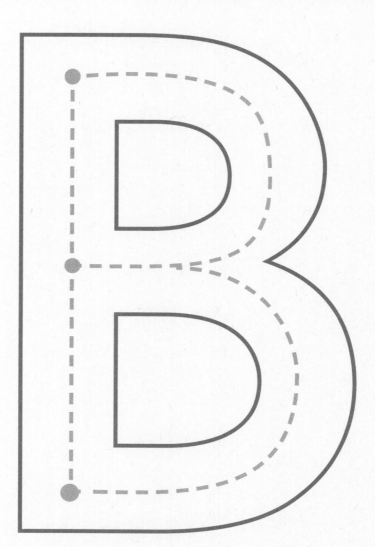

 Talk with your toddler about things that begin with the letter B.

Trace the letter C. Then color it.

Car

Cat

★ Talk with your toddler about things that begin with the letter C.

Trace the letter D. Then color it.

  **D**og  **D**oll

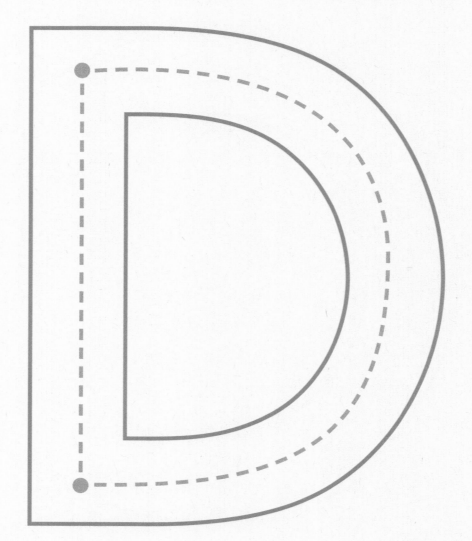

 Talk with your toddler about things that begin with the letter D.

Trace the letter E. Then color it.

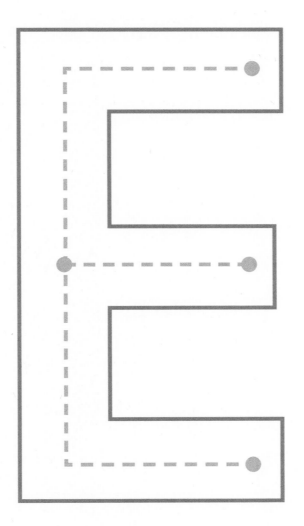

 Talk with your toddler about things that begin with the letter E.

Trace the letter F. Then color it.

F | Fish | Fan

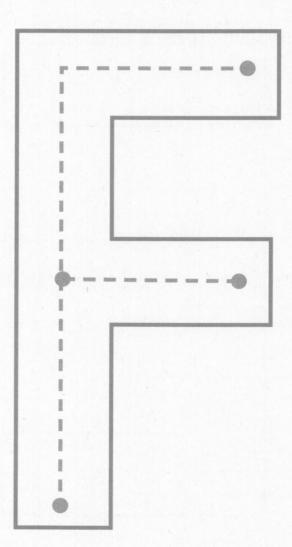

  Talk with your toddler about things that begin with the letter F.

Trace the letter G. Then color it.

Gorilla

Gift

Talk with your toddler about things that begin with the letter G.

Trace the letter H. Then color it.

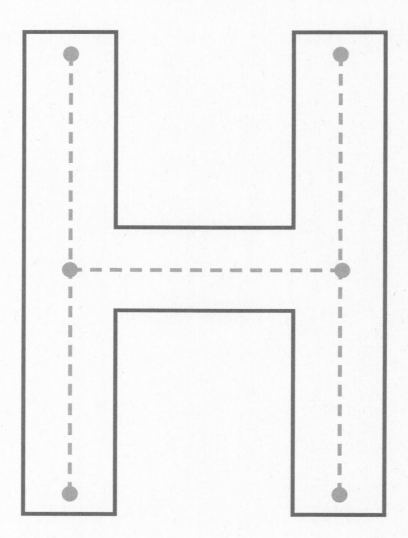

 Talk with your toddler about things that begin with the letter H.

Trace the letter I. Then color it.

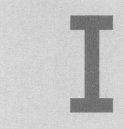  

Insect   Ice cream

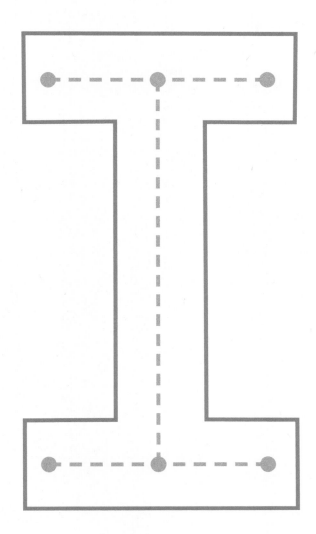

 Talk with your toddler about things that begin with the letter I.

Trace the letter J. Then color it.

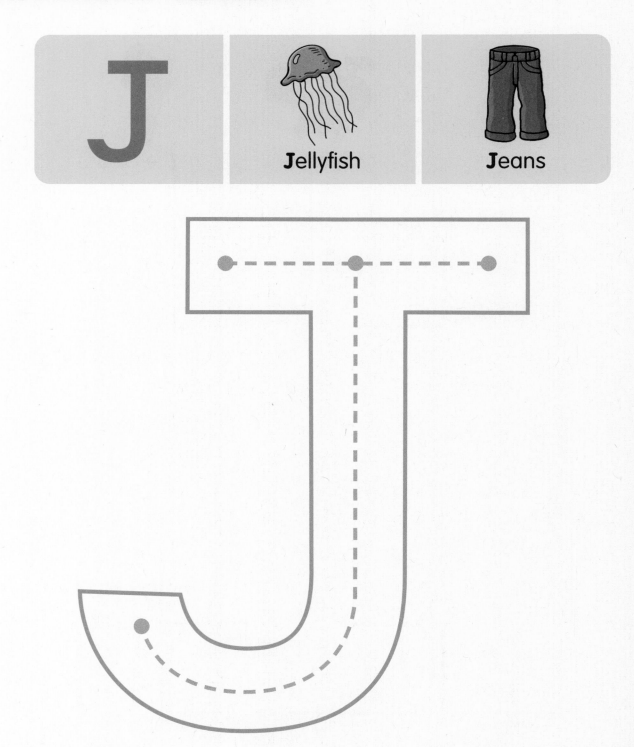

J | Jellyfish | Jeans

 Talk with your toddler about things that begin with the letter J.

Trace the letter K. Then color it.

K | Kangaroo | Kite

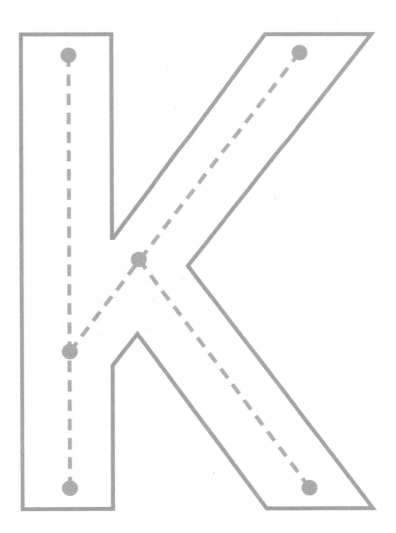

 Talk with your toddler about things that begin with the letter K.

Trace the letter L. Then color it.

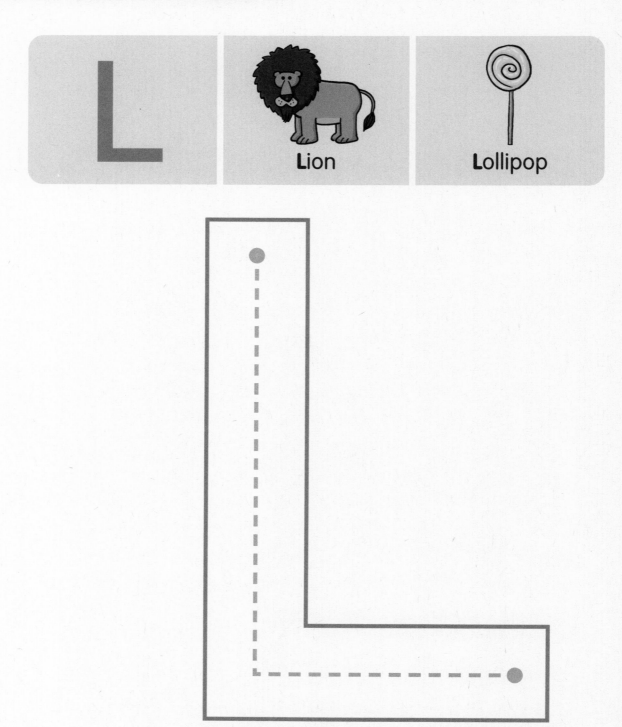

Lion

Lollipop

 Talk with your toddler about things that begin with the letter L.

Trace the letter M. Then color it.

Monkey

Mitten

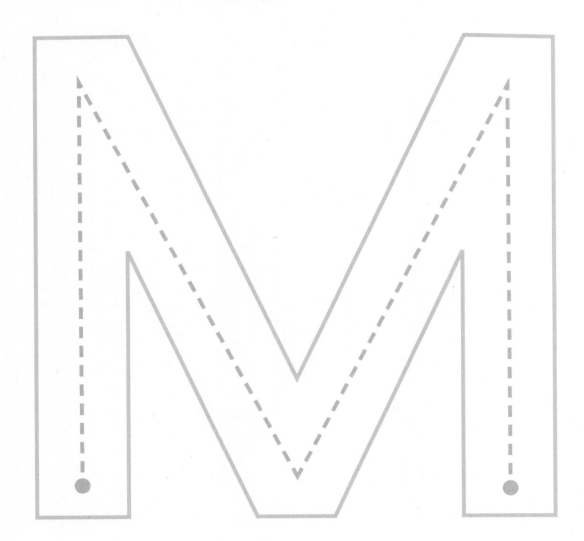

 Talk with your toddler about things that begin with the letter M.

Trace the letter N. Then color it.

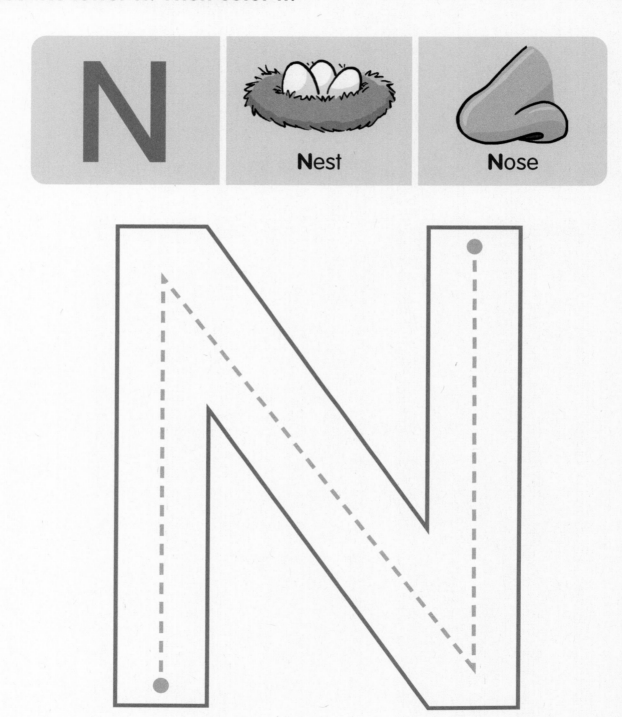

Nest

Nose

 Talk with your toddler about things that begin with the letter N.

Trace the letter O. Then color it.

Octopus

Orange

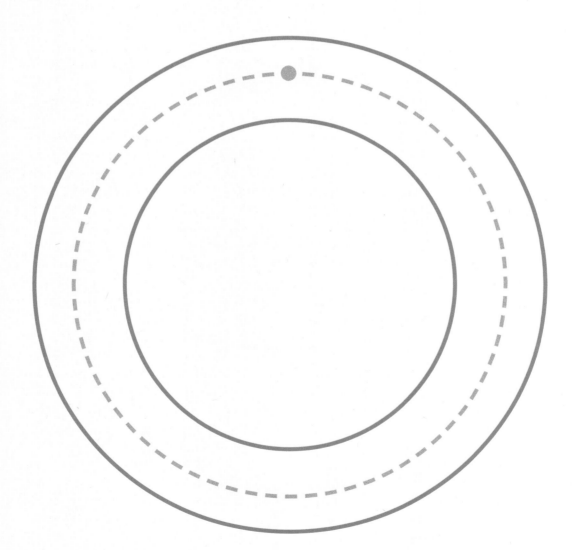

 Talk with your toddler about things that begin with the letter O.

© Scholastic Inc.

Trace the letter P. Then color it.

Pig

Pie

 Talk with your toddler about things that begin with the letter P.

Trace the letter Q. Then color it.

Queen

Quilt

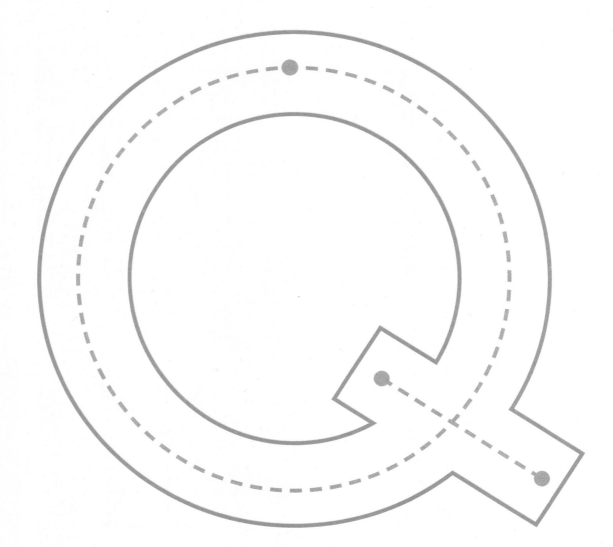

Talk with your toddler about things that begin with the letter Q.

Trace the letter R. Then color it.

Rabbit

Robot

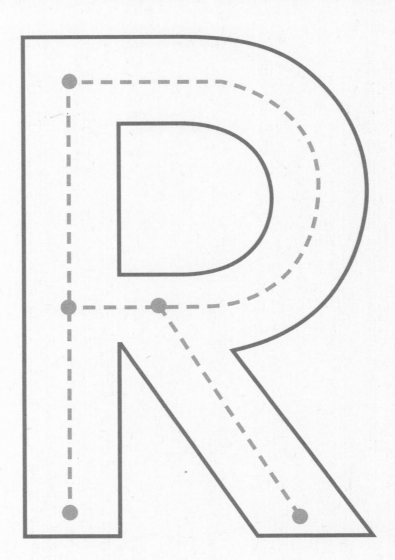

 Talk with your toddler about things that begin with the letter R.

Trace the letter S. Then color it.

Seal

Sock

Talk with your toddler about things that begin with the letter S.

Trace the letter T. Then color it.

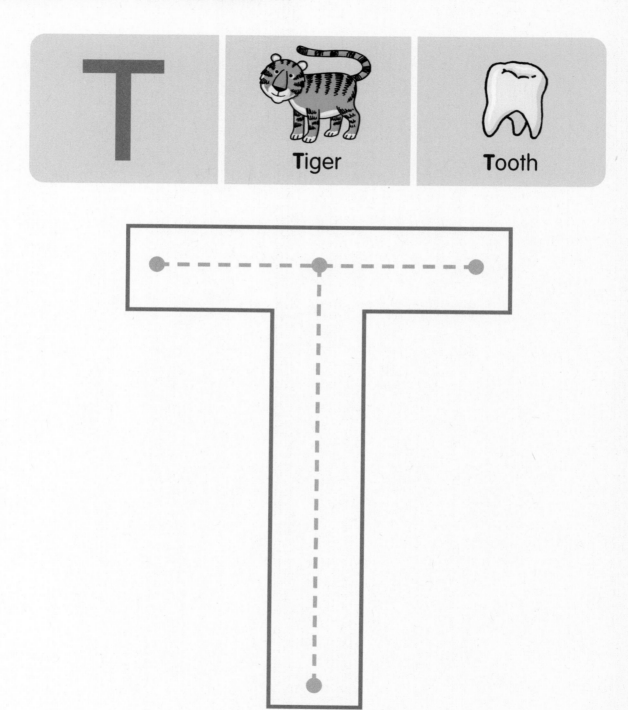

Tiger

Tooth

 Talk with your toddler about things that begin with the letter T.

Trace the letter U. Then color it.

Umbrella

Underwear

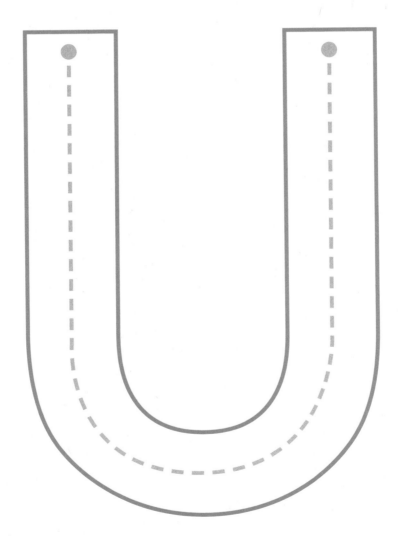

Talk with your toddler about things that begin with the letter U.

Trace the letter V. Then color it.

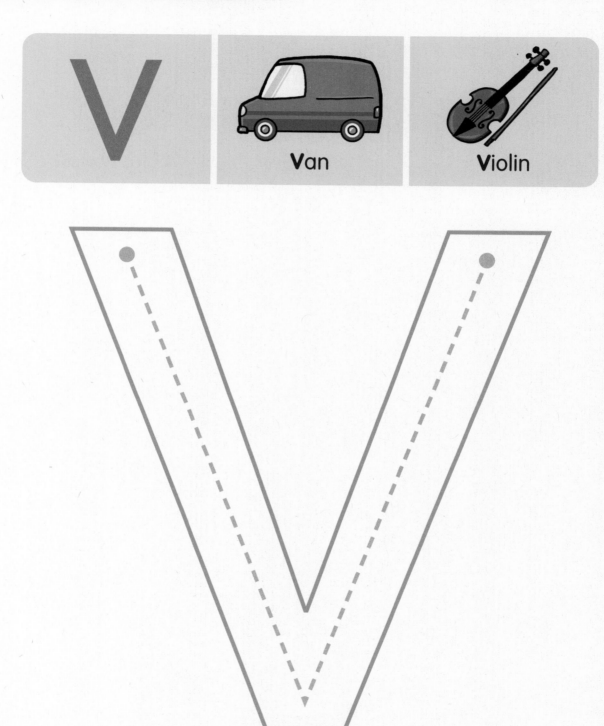

Van

Violin

Talk with your toddler about things that begin with the letter V.

Trace the letter W. Then color it.

Whale **W**atermelon

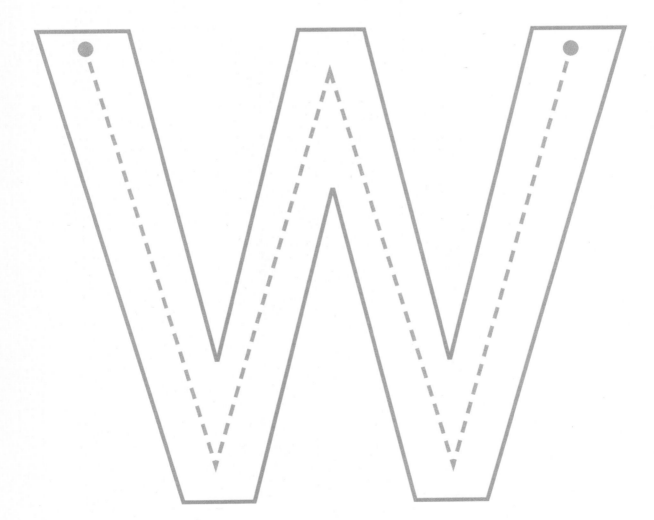

 Talk with your toddler about things that begin with the letter W.

Trace the letter X. Then color it.

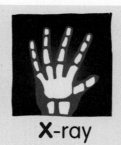

X-ray

Xylophone

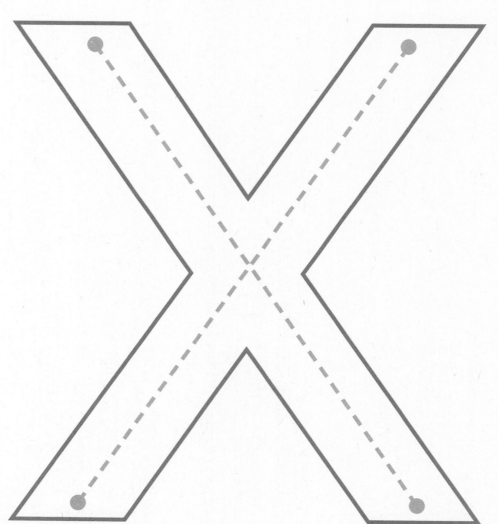

Talk with your toddler about things that begin with the letter X.

Trace the letter Y. Then color it.

Y   Yak   Yoyo

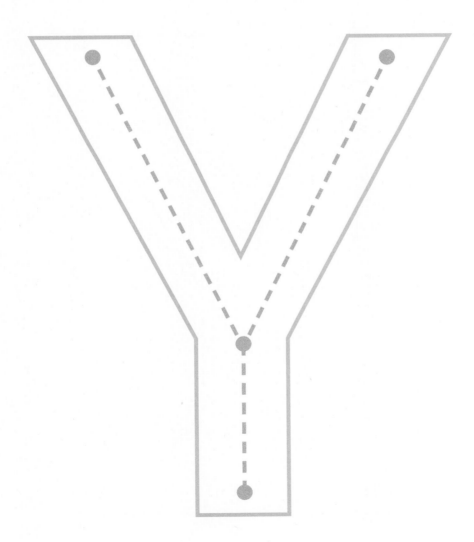

 Talk with your toddler about things that begin with the letter Y.

Trace the letter Z. Then color it.

Zebra

Zipper

 Talk with your toddler about things that begin with the letter Z.

·SCHOLASTIC SUCCESS WITH·
NUMBERS

★ This section will introduce your toddler to numbers 1–10. Read the directions aloud. Then invite him or her to trace the featured number.

★ Along with your toddler, count the number of items in the picture, such as one dinosaur, two children, or three plants.

★ Follow up the session with the starred EXTRA activity at the bottom of the page. This will help build your toddler's listening and speaking skills.

★ To reinforce learning, help your toddler count food items at meals, such as one pancake, two meatballs, or three grapes.

SUPPLIES: crayons or washable markers

Trace then color the number 1.

 Invite your toddler to finish this sentence: This page has 1

_____.

Trace then color the number 2.

 Invite your toddler to finish this sentence: This page has 2

_____.

Trace then color the number 3.

 Invite your toddler to finish this sentence: This page has 3

_____.

Trace then color the number 4.

 Invite your toddler to finish this sentence: This page has 4

_____.

Trace then color the number 5.

 Invite your toddler to finish this sentence: This page has 5

_____.

Trace then color the number 6.

Invite your toddler to finish this sentence: This page has 6

_____.

Trace then color the number 7.

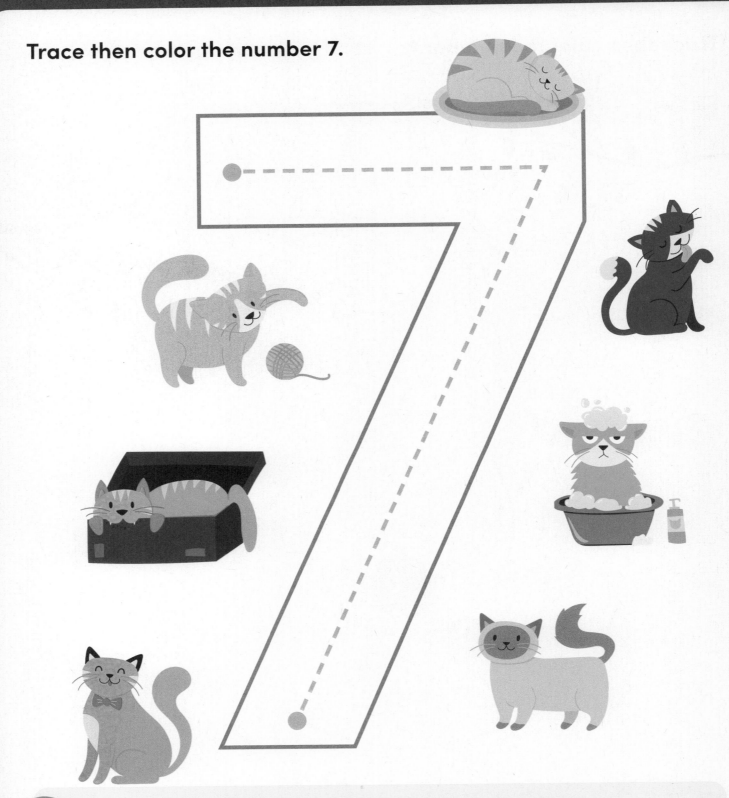

 Invite your toddler to finish this sentence: This page has 7

_____.

Trace then color the number 8.

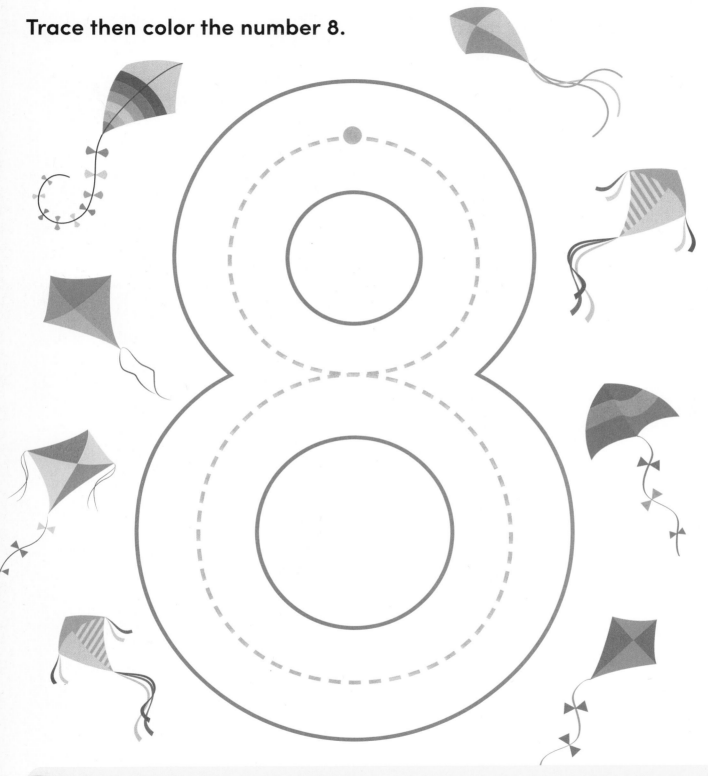

 Invite your toddler to finish this sentence: This page has 8

_____ .

Trace then color the number 9.

Invite your toddler to finish this sentence: This page has 9

_____.

Trace then color the number 10.

 Invite your toddler to finish this sentence: This page has 10

_____.

· SCHOLASTIC SUCCESS WITH ·

COLORS

★ This section will introduce your toddler to the colors red, blue, yellow, green, orange, purple, pink, brown, white, black, and gray. Read the directions aloud. Then invite your child to color the item pictured, such as apples, the appropriate color.

★ Point to the item in the picture, such as a green frog, and invite your toddler to tell you about it. Then you can take the opportunity to share your own age-appropriate fun facts, such as: *frogs can hop, frogs live in ponds, frogs say "Ribbit."*

★ Follow up the session with the starred EXTRA activity at the bottom of the page. This will help build your toddler's listening and speaking skills.

★ To reinforce learning, give your toddler crayons and paper for a free-drawing session. This simple activity will boost color recognition and fine motor skills. It will also activate your child's big imagination!

SUPPLIES: crayons or washable markers

Color the apples in the bowl red.

 Talk to your toddler about things that are red.

Color the whale in the ocean  blue.

Talk to your toddler about things that are blue.

Color the sun in the sky  **yellow.**

 Talk to your toddler about things that are yellow.

Color the frog on the lily pad green.

 Talk to your toddler about things that are green.

Color the pumpkin in the wheelbarrow orange.

 Talk to your toddler about things that are orange.

Color the pig in the puddle pink.

 Talk to your toddler about things that are pink.

Color the dinosaur in the park purple.

 Talk to your toddler about things that are purple.

Color the dog on the pillow brown.

 Talk to your toddler about things that are brown.

Color the unicorn in the garden **white.**

 Talk to your toddler about things that are white.

Color the cat on the mat black.

 Talk to your toddler about things that are black.

Color the elephant in the grass 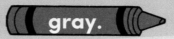 gray.

 Talk to your toddler about things that are gray.

Color the rainbow in the sky lots of colors.

⭐ Talk to your toddler about things that are lots of colors.

SCHOLASTIC SUCCESS WITH

SHAPES

★ This section will introduce your toddler to circles, squares, triangles, rectangles, ovals, diamonds, hexagons, and more.

★ Read the directions aloud. Point to the item in the picture—such as a pizza—and announce its shape, such as a *circle*. Discuss other items of the same shape. Then invite your toddler to color it.

★ Follow up the session with the starred EXTRA activity at the bottom of the page. This will help build your toddler's listening and speaking skills.

★ To reinforce learning, draw an array of shapes on paper for your child to color and/or trace. Before bed, point out shapes in his or her bedroom, such as a square book, a rectangular window, or an oval rug.

SUPPLIES: crayons or washable markers

The pizza is a circle. Color it.

 Talk to your toddler about things that are a circle shape.

The present is a square. Color it.

 Talk to your toddler about things that are a square shape.

The hat is a triangle. Color it.

 Talk to your toddler about things that are a triangle shape.

The book is a rectangle. Color it.

THE RUNAWAY RECTANGLE

By Sam Shape

 Talk to your toddler about things that are a rectangle shape.

The kite is a diamond shape. Color it.

 Talk to your toddler about things that are a diamond shape.

The picture is an oval. Color it.

 Talk to your toddler about things that are an oval shape.

The web is a hexagon. Color it.

⭐ Talk to your toddler about things that are a hexagon shape.

The sea star is a star shape. Color it.

 Talk to your toddler about things that are a star shape.

The Valentine is a heart shape. Color it.

 Talk to your toddler about things that are a heart shape.

The moon is a crescent shape. Color it.

 Talk to your toddler about things that are a crescent shape.

· SCHOLASTIC SUCCESS WITH ·

CUTTING & PASTING

★ This section will introduce your toddler to cutting and pasting, which will build important fine motor skills. Read the directions aloud. Then invite him or her to cut and paste the shapes to create adorable animals! **Always supervise children when using scissors.**

★ If your toddler is too young to cut out a shape effectively, feel free to guide his or her hand when using the safety scissors. Or, do the cutting yourself. The gluing, too, can be done with or without your help. Cutting and pasting are skills that takes time and practice, so be patient and focus on fun.

★ Follow up the session with the starred EXTRA activity at the bottom of the page. This will help build your toddler's listening and speaking skills.

★ To reinforce learning, draw an array of large shapes on paper for your toddler to cut, color, and paste onto a large sheet of paper. Hang his/her creations in a shape gallery on a festive bulletin board or your refrigerator.

SUPPLIES: safety scissors and nontoxic glue stick

Cut out the circle. Paste it on page 111.

Paste the circle here. What animal do you see?

 Talk to your toddler about cats. Share words that describe them.

Make the sound that a cat makes.

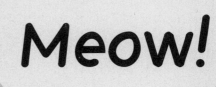

 Challenge your toddler to say "MEOW" quietly and then loudly.

Cut out the square. Paste it on page 115.

Paste the square here. What animal do you see?

 Talk to your toddler about dogs. Share words that describe them.

Make the sound that a dog makes.

 Challenge your toddler to say "RUFF" quietly and then loudly.

Cut out the triangle. Paste it on page 119.

Paste the triangle here. What animal do you see?

 Talk to your toddler about snakes. Share words that describe them.

Make the sound that a snake makes.

Challenge your toddler to say "SSSSSSSSS" quietly and then loudly.

Cut out the rectangle. Paste it on page 123.

Paste the rectangle here. What animal do you see?

 Talk to your toddler about horses. Share words that describe them.

Make the sound that a horse makes.

 Challenge your toddler to say "NEIGH" quietly and then loudly.

Cut out the oval. Paste it on page 127.

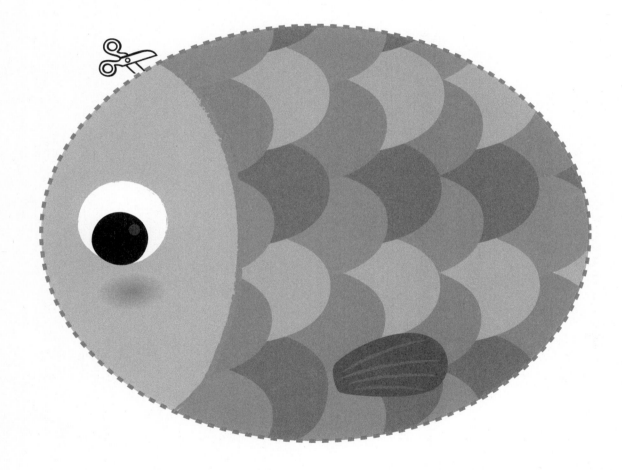

Paste the oval here. What animal do you see?

 Talk to your toddler about fish. Share words that describe them.

Make the sound that a fish makes.

 Challenge your toddler to say "GLUB" quietly and then loudly.

Cut out the diamond shape. Paste it on page 131.

Paste the diamond shape here. What animal do you see?

 Talk to your toddler about monkeys. Share words that describe them.

Make the sound that a monkey makes.

 Challenge your toddler to say "EEEE-EEEE" quietly and then loudly.

Cut out the hexagon. Paste it on page 135.

Paste the hexagon here. What animal do you see?

 Talk to your toddler about lions. Share words that describe them.

Make the sound that a lion makes.

 Challenge your toddler to say "ROAR" quietly and then loudly.

Cut out the star shape. Paste it on page 139.

Paste the star shape here. What animal do you see?

 Talk to your toddler about sea stars. Share words that describe them.

Make the sound that a sea star makes.

Splash!

 Challenge your toddler to say "SPLASH" quietly and then loudly.

Cut out the heart shape. Paste it on page 143.

Paste the heart shape here. What animal do you see?

 Talk to your toddler about owls. Share words that describe them.

Make the sound that an owl makes.

 Challenge your toddler to say "HOOT" quietly and then loudly.

Cut out the crescent shape. Paste it on page 147.

Paste the crescent shape here. What animal do you see?

 Talk to your toddler about frogs. Share words that describe them.

Make the sound that a frog makes.

Ribbit!

 Challenge your toddler to say "RIBBIT" quietly and then loudly.

BASIC CONCEPTS

★ This section will introduce your toddler to important basic concepts such as *big and small, short and tall, up and down, in and out, happy and sad*, and more.

★ Read the directions aloud. Then invite your child to color the items on the page as directed. If your toddler struggles to understand the basic concept being presented—such as *up and down*—point to each item and say "up" or "down."

★ Follow up the session with the starred EXTRA activity at the bottom of the page. This will help build your toddler's listening and speaking skills.

★ To reinforce learning, point out opposites in your home and neighborhood, such as a stuffed animal that is big and a stuffed animal that is small or a cat that is inside and a cat that is outside.

SUPPLIES: crayons or washable markers

Color the monster that is big  red.
Color the monster that is small blue.

 Invite your toddler to pretend to be a monster.

Color the cat that is up **black.**
Color the cat that is down **white.**

 Invite your toddler to pretend to be a cat.

Color the snake that is long  brown.
Color the snake that is short purple.

⭐ Invite your toddler to pretend to be a snake.

Color the animal that is tall yellow.
Color the animal that is short green.

 What two animals do you see in the picture?

Color the bee that is inside  yellow.
Color the bee that is outside orange.

 Invite your toddler to pretend to be a bee.

Color the balloon that is happy  yellow.
Color the balloon that is sad blue.

 Talk with your toddler about things that make him/her happy.

Color the dragon that is big purple.

Color the dragon that is small red.

 Talk about things that are small. Find some in your home.

Color the monkey that is up **brown.**

Color the monkey that is down **gray.**

 Invite your toddler to pretend to be a monkey.

Color the car that is long  yellow.
Color the car that is short blue.

⭐ Invite your toddler to pretend to be a car.

Color the slide that is tall green.

Color the slide that is short red.

Ask your toddler, "Which slide would you like to go on?"

Color the robot that is inside orange.
Color the robot that is outside pink.

 Invite your toddler to pretend to be a robot.

Color the flower that is happy **red.**
Color the flower that is sad **blue.**

 Talk to your toddler about things that make him/her sad.

SCHOLASTIC SUCCESS WITH

MATCHING

★ This section will introduce your toddler to the important concept of one-to-one correspondence, otherwise known as *matching*.

★ Read the directions aloud and name each pictured item. Then invite your child to draw lines to make matches. **Note:** A dashed line is provided for the first match. If your toddler struggles to draw straight lines, feel free to guide his or her hand.

★ Follow up the session with the starred EXTRA activity at the bottom of the page. This will help build your toddler's listening and speaking skills.

★ To reinforce learning, play a game in which you place two like or unlike items on a table—such as two apples or an apple and an orange. Then challenge your toddler to tell you whether the items in each set are alike or different.

SUPPLIES: crayons or washable markers

Draw lines to match the fruits.

 Challenge your toddler to name these fruits. Can he/she think of others?

Draw lines to match the toys.

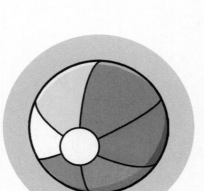

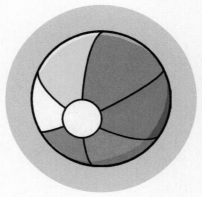

 Challenge your toddler to name these toys. Can he/she think of more?

Draw lines to match the vegetables.

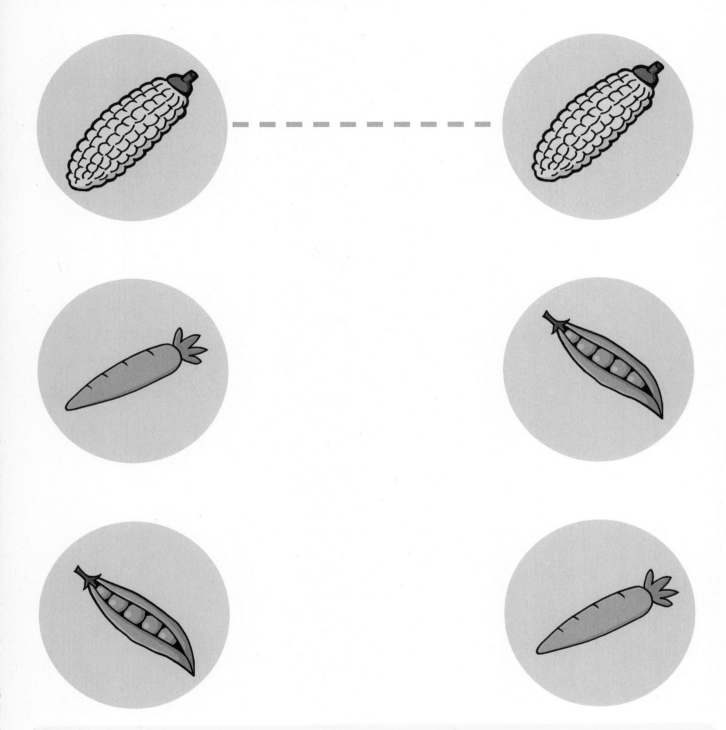

 Challenge your toddler to name these vegetables. Can he/she think of more?

Draw lines to match the things that go.

 Challenge your toddler to name these things that go. Can he/she think of more?

Draw lines to match the farm animals.

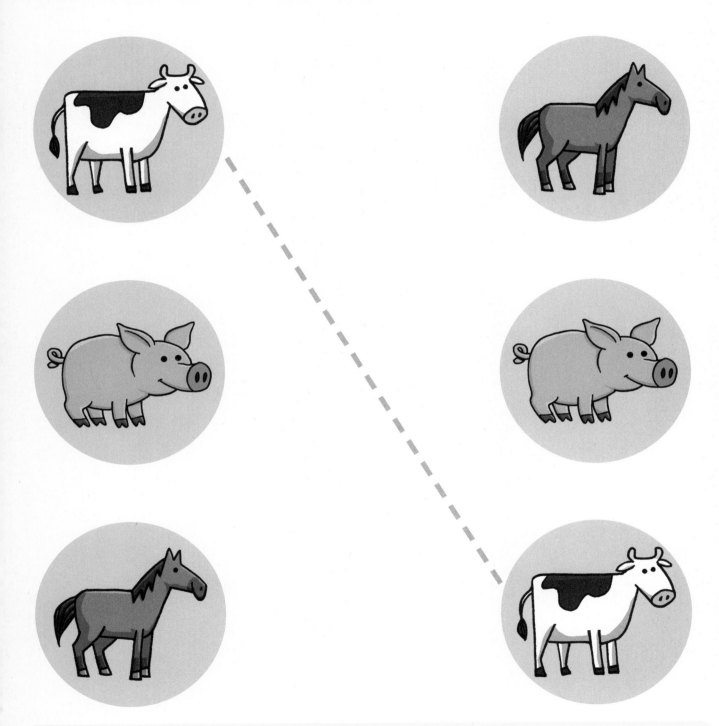

 Challenge your toddler to name these farm animals. Can he/she think of more?

Draw lines to match the helpers.

 Challenge your toddler to name these helpers. Can he/she think of more?

Draw lines to match the parts of the face.

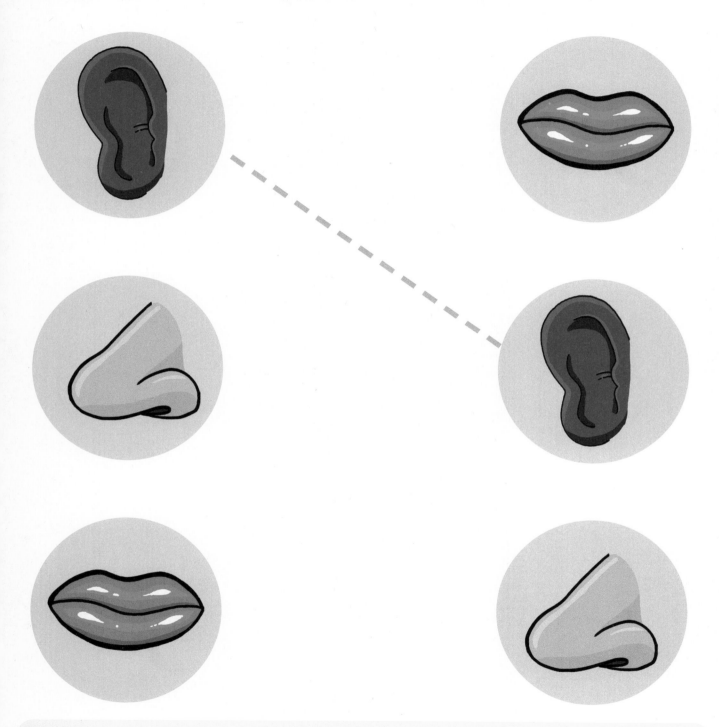

 Challenge your toddler to name these parts of a face. Can he/she think of more?

Draw lines to match the birds.

 Challenge your toddler to name these birds. Can he/she think of more?

Draw lines to match the food.

Challenge your toddler to name these foods. Can he/she think of more?

Draw lines to match the pets.

 Challenge your toddler to name these pets. Can he/she think of more?

Draw lines to match the clothes.

 - - - - - - - - -

 Challenge your toddler to name these clothing items. Can he/she think of more?

Draw lines to match the things in the sky.

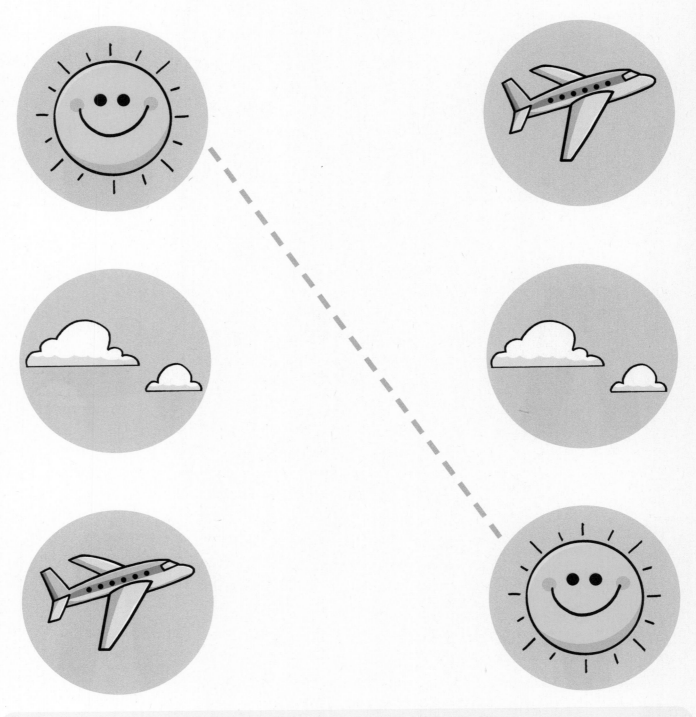

 Challenge your toddler to name these things in the sky. Can he/she think of more?

Draw lines to match the treats.

 Challenge your toddler to name these treats. Can he/she think of more?

Draw lines to match these big animals.

 Challenge your toddler to name these big animals. Can he/she think of more?

Draw lines to match these small animals.

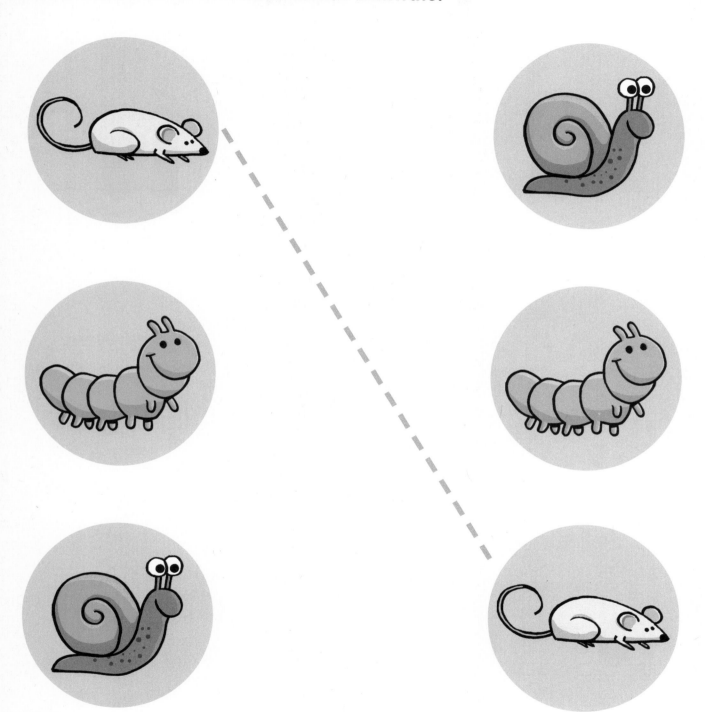

 Challenge your toddler to name these small animals. Can he/she think of more?

Draw lines to match the homes.

 Ask your toddler who lives in a castle. Does he/she see a castle on the page?

Draw lines to match the flowers.

 Ask your toddler what his/her favorite flower is. Can he/she name other flowers?

SCHOLASTIC SUCCESS WITH

SORTING

★ This section will introduce your toddler to sorting AND reinforce cutting and pasting skills. Read the directions. Then, invite him or her to cut out the two animals at the bottom of the page and paste each with the correct group. **Always supervise children when using scissors.**

★ If your toddler is too young to cut effectively, feel free to guide his or her hand when using the safety scissors. The gluing, too, can be done with or without your help. Cutting and pasting are skills that take time and practice, so be patient and focus on fun.

★ Follow up the session with the starred EXTRA activities at the bottom and back of the page. This will help build your toddler's conversational and critical-thinking skills.

★ To reinforce learning, play a game in which you place two groups of objects on a table—such as apples and oranges. Then, challenge your toddler to sort more apples and oranges into each group. Repeat the activities with different objects such as crayons/markers or paper plates/paper cups.

SUPPLIES: crayons or washable markers, safety scissors, nontoxic glue stick

Cut out the pets at the bottom of the page. Then, paste each in the right group.

⭐ Talk to your toddler about how cats and dogs are alike and different.

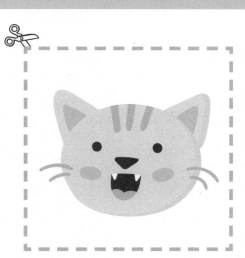 

Pretend to be a cat, then a dog. Challenge your toddler to copy you.

Meow!

Ruff!

Cut out the farm animals at the bottom of the page. Then, paste each in the right group.

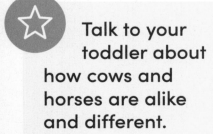

Talk to your toddler about how cows and horses are alike and different.

Pretend to be a cow, then a horse. Challenge your toddler to copy you.

Moo!

Neigh!

Cut out the insects at the bottom of the page. Then, paste each in the right group.

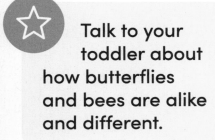 Talk to your toddler about how butterflies and bees are alike and different.

Pretend to be a butterfly, then a bee. Challenge your toddler to copy you.

Cut out the birds at the bottom of the page. Then, paste each in the right group.

⭐ Talk to your toddler about how penguins and ducks are alike and different.

Pretend to be a penguin, then a duck. Challenge your toddler to copy you.

Cut out the small animals at the bottom of the page. Then, paste each in the right group.

 Talk to your toddler about how frogs and mice are alike and different.

Pretend to be a frog, then a mouse. Challenge your toddler to copy you.

Cut out the jungle animals at the bottom of the page. Then, paste each in the right group.

 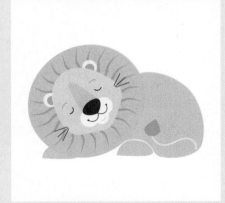

⭐ Talk to your toddler about how lions and elephants are alike and different.

Pretend to be a elephant, then a lion. Challenge your toddler to copy you.

Roar!

Trumpet!

Cut out the forest animals at the bottom of the page. Then, paste each in the right group.

⭐ Talk to your toddler about how owls and bears are alike and different.

Pretend to be an owl, then a bear. Challenge your toddler to copy you.

Hoot!

Grrrrrrr!

Cut out the ocean animals at the bottom of the page. Then, paste each in the right group.

⭐ Talk to your toddler about how fish and crabs are alike and different.

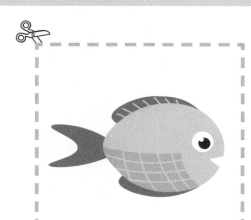 

Pretend to be a fish, then a crab. Challenge your toddler to copy you.

EASY RHYMES

★ Nursery rhymes are fun and packed with learning! Inviting your toddler to chant along to "Jack and Jill" builds oral language skills and develops early vocabulary skills. In addition, and perhaps most important, these "sticky" rhymes will help your child begin to understand the way that words work, setting the stage for reading success.

★ Read each rhyme slowly, clearly, and with verve— encouraging your toddler to join in. There is no such thing as repeating a rhyme too many times.

★ Try the starred EXTRA activity at the bottom of the page, which enriches the rhyme with a simple fingerplay, movement, or other activity.

★ To extend learning, complete the companion page. It provides an illustration to accompany the rhyme, plus a skill-building activity. **Tip:** Looking for more nursery rhymes to share with your toddler? Simply search for more on the internet.

SUPPLIES: crayons or washable markers

Say the rhyme with your toddler.

Humpty Dumpty

Humpty Dumpty

sat on a wall.

Humpty Dumpty

had a great fall.

All the king's horses

and all the king's men

couldn't put Humpty

together again.

On *Humpty Dumpty sat on a wall*, fold your arms to make a wall. On *had a great fall*, roll your arms. On *all the king's horses*, hold pretend horse reins. On *couldn't put Humpty together again*, shake your head *no*. Invite your toddler to copy you.

Help Humpty by putting a  on each of his broken parts.

 Talk about ways your toddler can help a friend feel better, such as by offering a Band-Aid or a hug.

Say the rhyme with your toddler.

Peek-a-Boo

Peek-a-boo!

Peek-a-boo!

_____ sees me.
toddler's name

I see _____, too!
toddler's name

 Play peek-a-boo with your toddler as you read the rhyme.

Trace the stripes on the T-shirt.

 Invite your toddler to play peek-a-boo with a favorite stuffed toy. For example, hold a teddy bear in front of your face and say: *Peek-a-boo! Peek-a-boo! <u>Leo</u> sees <u>Teddy</u>. <u>Teddy</u> sees <u>Leo</u>, too!*

Say the rhyme with your toddler.

Pat-a-Cake

Pat-a-cake, pat-a-cake,

baker's man.

Bake me a cake as fast

as you can.

Pat it and prick it and

mark it with a *B*.

Put it in the oven

for baby and me.

  As you say the rhyme, have your toddler clap his/her hands, then clap yours. As he/she becomes more adept, add more hand motions, such as patting the dough or marking the cake with a *B*.

Trace the B and color it   blue.

 B is for *Baby*. Talk about other words that begin with *B*.

Say the rhyme with your toddler.

Hickory, Dickory, Dock

Hickory, dickory, dock,

the mouse ran up the clock.

The clock struck one,

the mouse ran down—

hickory, dickory, dock.

 On *the mouse ran up the clock*, run your fingers up your toddler's arm. On *the clock struck one*, clap. On *the mouse ran down*, run your fingers down your toddler's arm.

Color the mouse gray.

⭐ **Talk about mice with your toddler. Ask:** *What other animals are small?*

Say the rhyme with your toddler.

Teddy Bear, Teddy Bear

Teddy bear, teddy bear,

turn around!

Teddy bear, teddy bear,

touch the ground!

Teddy bear, teddy bear,

jump up high!

Teddy bear, teddy bear,

touch the sky!

 Challenge your toddler to pretend to be the teddy bear by turning around, touching the ground, and jumping up high on cue.

Color the teddy bear orange.

⭐ Invite your toddler to use an actual teddy bear to act out the rhyme as you read it.

Say the rhyme with your toddler.

Little Red Wagon

Bumping up and down

in a little red wagon.

Bumping up and down

in a little red wagon.

Up, down, all around—

won't you be my buddy?

 Sit your toddler on your lap, bumping him/her up and down on your knees as you read the rhyme. Share the rhyme again, each time reading it a bit faster.

Color the wagon red.

 If you have a wagon, treat your toddler to a ride. If you don't, use a big box to make a pretend wagon.

Say the rhyme with your toddler.

Here Is a Bunny

Here is a bunny

with ears so funny

and fur of fuzzy brown.

When a noise he hears,

he pricks his ears.

And jumps in a hole

in the ground!

On *ears so funny*, hold two fingers above your head like bunny ears. On *when a noise he hears*, cup a hand to your ear. On *jumps in a hole*, jump down on the ground. Challenge your toddler to do the same.

Color the bunny brown.

 Invite your toddler to pretend he/she is a bunny and hop around inside or outside.

Say the rhyme with your toddler.

Rub-a-Dub-Dub

Rub-a-dub-dub,

three pals in a tub.

And who do you

think they be?

A dog, a cat, and a kid

named _____.

toddler's name

All of them float

on the sea!

Change the animals in the fifth line to new creatures, such as *a frog, a fairy, and a kid named Alyssa*. Then, share the new version with your toddler.

Help your toddler color the paper-doll shape to resemble him— or herself.

 Talk about—and demonstrate!—things that can float on water, such as a toy boat or a rubber ducky.

Say the rhyme with your toddler.

Jack-in-the-Box

Jack-in-the-box,

jack-in-the-box

sits so still.

Will you pop out?

Yes, I will!

Invite your child to pretend to be a jack-in-the-box by crouching down low on *sits so still*, then springing up high on *Yes, I will!*

Color the box  pink.

 If you have a jack-in-the-box, share it with your toddler. If not, watch an online video of one.

Say the rhyme with your toddler.

Zoom, Zoom, Zoom!

Zoom, zoom, zoom!

We're going to the moon.

If you want to take a trip,

climb aboard my rocket ship.

Zoom, zoom, zoom!

We're going to the moon.

5, 4, 3, 2, 1—

Blast off!

Make a rocket ship out of a toilet-paper tube, inviting your toddler to "blast off" at the end of the rhyme.

Color the rocket ship green.

⭐ Read an easy book about rocket ships. Then, talk about the topic with your toddler.

Say the rhyme with your toddler.

Jack and Jill

Jack and Jill

went up the hill

to fetch a pail of water.

Jack fell down

and broke his crown,

and Jill came tumbling after.

 On *Jack and Jill went up the hill*, move your left and right thumbs upward as if climbing. On *Jack fell down and broke his crown*, swirl your left thumb down as if falling. On *Jill came tumbling after*, do the same with your right thumb. Invite your toddler to copy you.

Color the well  purple. Then, make a wish.

⭐ Talk to your toddler about easy ways to stay safe outside, such as always holding a grown-up's hand.

Say the rhyme with your toddler.

Hey, Diddle, Diddle

Hey, diddle, diddle,

the cat and the fiddle,

the cow jumped

over the moon.

The little dog laughed

to see such a sight.

And the dish ran away

with the spoon.

 Act out the rhyme with items you have in your home, such as a toy (or stuffed) cat, cow, and dog and/or a plastic dish and spoon.

Color the moon yellow.

 Use this picture to make up a simple story about one or all of the characters shown.

Say the rhyme with your toddler.

Little Boy Blue

Little boy blue,

come blow your horn.

The sheep's in the meadow,

the cow's in the corn.

But where is the boy

who looks after the sheep?

He's under a haystack,

fast asleep.

 On the last two lines of the rhyme, rest your head on your hands, pretend to fall asleep, and say ZZZZZZZZZ. Invite your toddler to do the same.

Color the little boy blue.

⭐ Why do children take naps? Talk about it with your toddler.

Say the rhyme with your toddler.

Little Miss Muffet

Little Miss Muffet

sat on a tuffet,

eating her curds and whey.

Along came a spider,

who sat down beside her

and frightened

Miss Muffet away.

 Change *Little Miss Muffet* to someone else—dad, grandma, your dog, a prince—then reread the revised rhyme. (NOTE: If changing to a male, you will also have to change each *her* to *him*.)

Color the spider  orange.

Spiders are amazing! Show your toddler an online video of one spinning a web.

Say the rhyme with your toddler.

One, Two, Buckle My Shoe

One, two, buckle my shoe.

Three, four, shut the door.

Five, six, pick up sticks.

Seven, eight, lay them straight.

Nine, ten, a big red hen.

 As you read each number, hold up two fingers, four fingers, six fingers, eight fingers, then ten fingers. At the end, invite your toddler to strut around like a hen saying, "CLUCK, CLUCK, CLUCK!"

Color the hen red.

1 2 3

5 6 7 8

9 10

 Grab ten small objects, such as crayons or toy cars. Practice counting them with your toddler.

Say the rhyme with your toddler.

Roses Are Red

Roses are red.

Violets are blue.

Sugar is sweet

and so are you!

Elephants are big.

Butterflies are not.

I love _____

toddler's name

a lot, lot, lot!

 Replace *roses* and *violets* with other things that are red and blue, such as *apples* and *whales*. Replace *elephants* and *butterflies* with other things that are big and small, such as *dinosaurs* and *fairies*.

Trace and color the hearts pink.

 Talk to your toddler about other things that are red and blue and big and small.

MORE FINE MOTOR SKILLS

★ This section will continue to develop your toddler's fine motor skills. Read the directions aloud. Then demonstrate how to draw lightning bolts, cookies, mountains, and more.

★ Remember, toddlers are just learning how to use a crayon, so don't worry if their attempt at cookies looks more like teardrops. The important thing is to promote practice and boost confidence.

★ Follow up the session with the starred EXTRA activity at the bottom of the page. This will help build your toddler's listening and speaking skills.

★ To reinforce learning, provide blank paper and fingerpaints. Then invite your toddler to have fun and paint whatever he or she wants. Proudly display the creations on a festive bulletin board or your refrigerator.

SUPPLIES: crayons or washable markers

Draw more stripes on the hat.

 Talk to your toddler about different types of hats.

Draw more snow falling down from the sky.

 Talk to your toddler about about snow. Is it hot or cold?

Draw more spots on the slinky snake.

 Talk to your toddler about snakes. Do they have arms and legs?

Draw more lightning in the sky.

 Talk to your toddler about thunder and lightning. What sound does thunder make?

Draw more legs on the creepy-crawly.

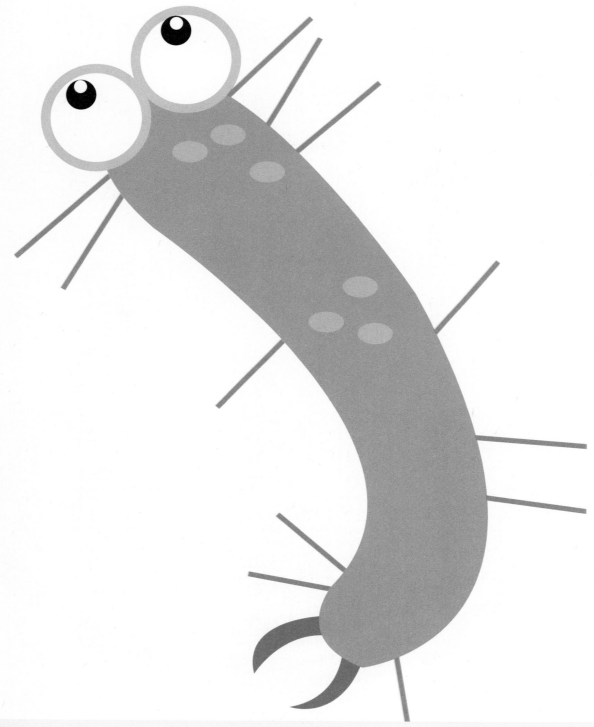

 Talk to your toddler about bugs. Are they big or small?

Draw more seeds on the watermelon.

 Talk about fruit. What is your toddler's favorite?

Draw more cookies on the cow's plate.

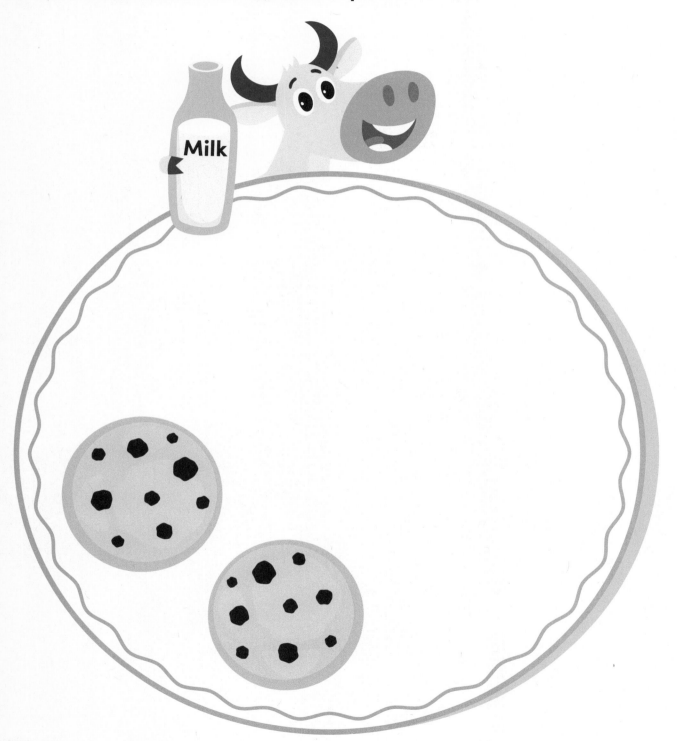

 Talk to your toddler about cows. What drink do they make?

Draw more scoops on the ice cream cones.

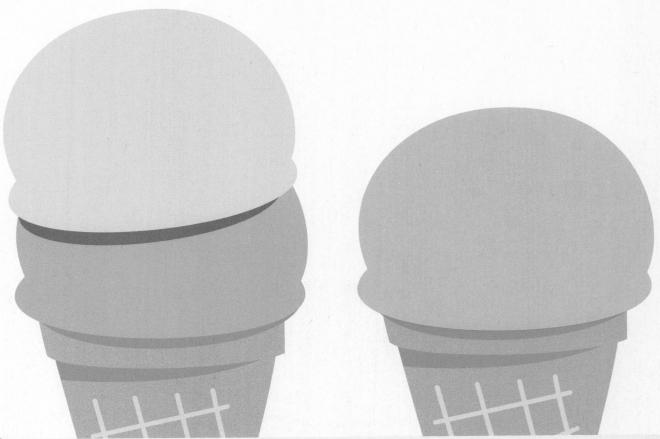

 Talk to your toddler about ice cream. What is his/her favorite flavor?

Draw more mountains in the desert.

 Talk to your toddler about mountains. Are they tall or short?

Draw more happy faces on the circles.

 Talk to your toddler about happiness. What makes him/her happy?

Draw more sad faces on the circles.

 Talk to your toddler about sadness. What makes him/her sad?

This silly monster has lots of eyes. Draw some more.

 Talk to your toddler about monsters. Are they real or pretend?

Draw more eggs in the nest.

 Talk to your toddler about eggs. Which animals lay eggs?

· SCHOLASTIC SUCCESS WITH ·
MORE TRACING

★ This section will continue to develop your toddler's tracing skills. Read the directions aloud. Then demonstrate how to trace waves, zigzags, shapes, and more.

★ If your toddler struggles to trace the dashed images, feel free to guide his or her hand.

★ Follow up the session with the starred EXTRA activity at the bottom of the page. This will help build your toddler's listening and speaking skills.

★ To reinforce learning, draw lines and shapes in the sand of a sandbox or at the beach. Then invite your toddler to copy them with his or her fingers.

SUPPLIES: crayons or washable markers

Trace the straight lines.

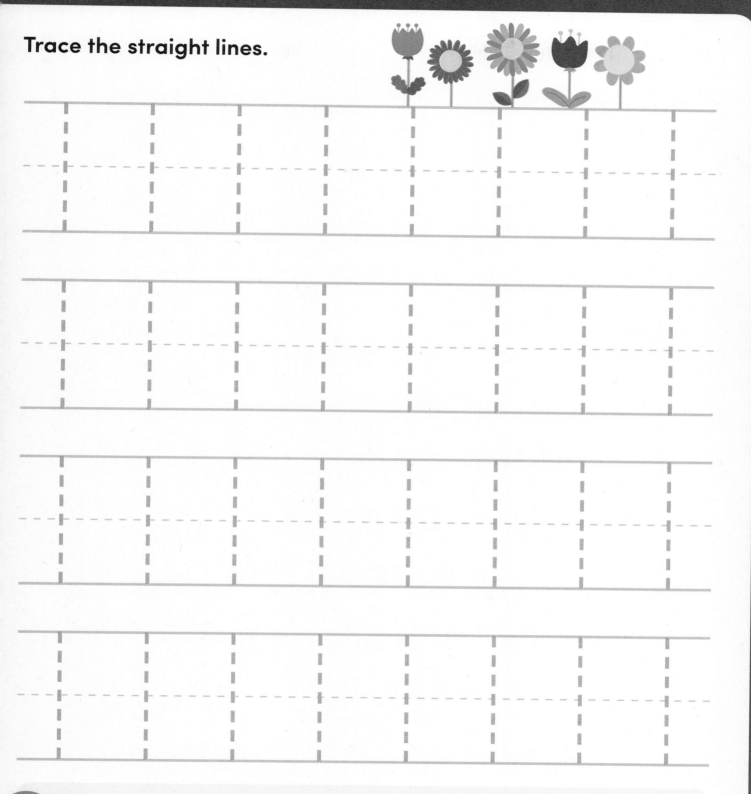

Can you and your toddler find more straight lines in your home or neighborhood?

Trace the wavy lines.

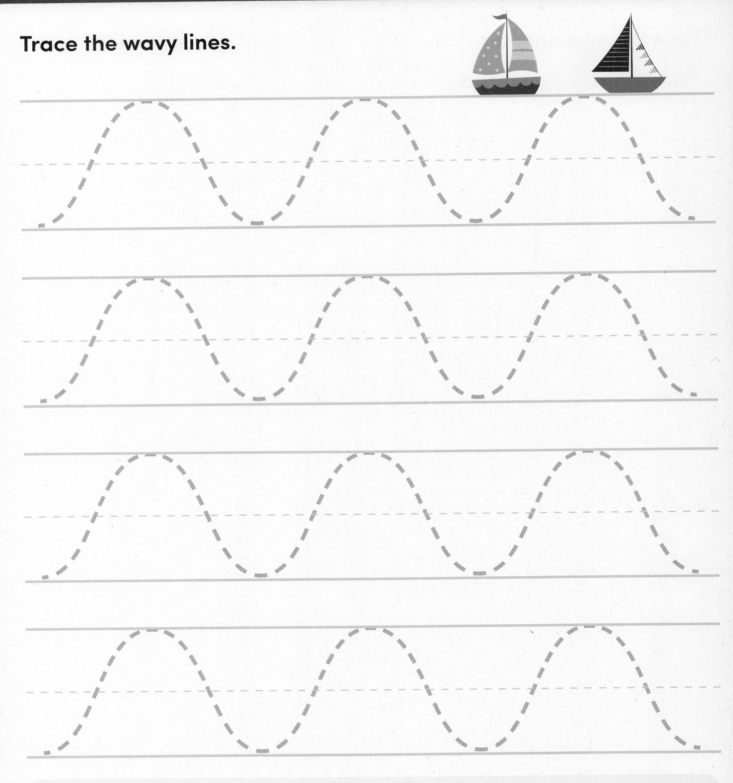

Can you and your toddler find more wavy lines in your home or neighborhood?

Trace the zigzag lines.

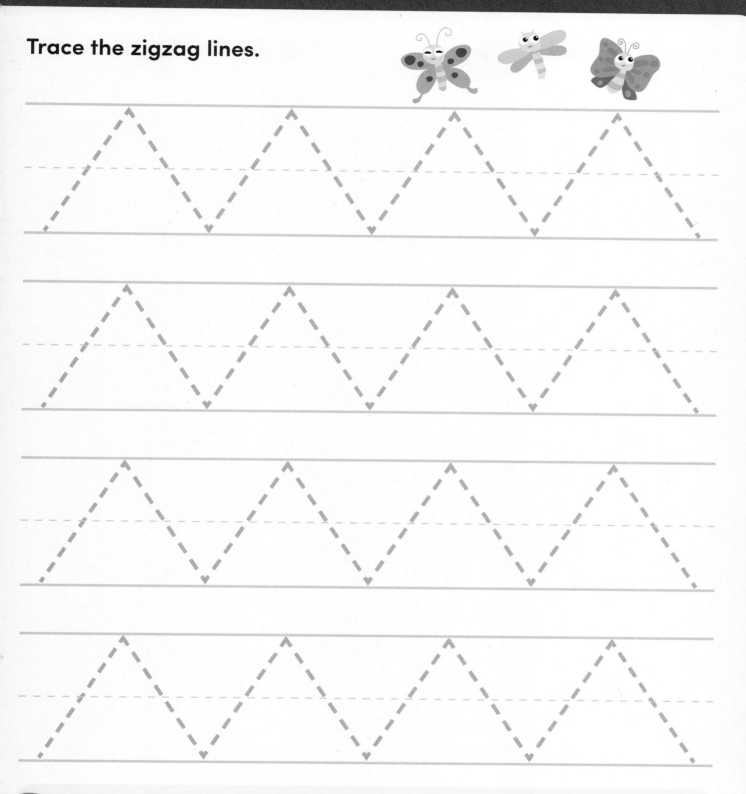

 Can you and your toddler find more zigzag lines in your home or neighborhood?

Trace the circles.

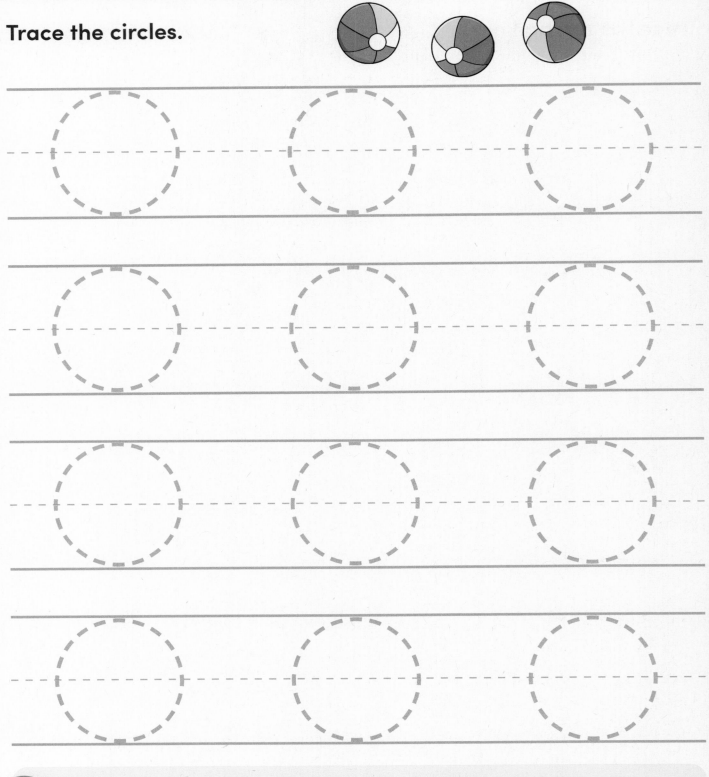

 Can you and your toddler find more circle shapes in your home or neighborhood?

Trace the squares.

 Can you and your toddler find more square shapes in your home or neighborhood?

Trace the triangles.

 Can you and your toddler find more triangle shapes in your home or neighborhood?

Trace the rectangles.

Can you and your toddler find more rectangle shapes in your home or neighborhood?

Trace the diamonds.

 Can you and your toddler find more diamond shapes in your home or neighborhood?

Trace the ovals.

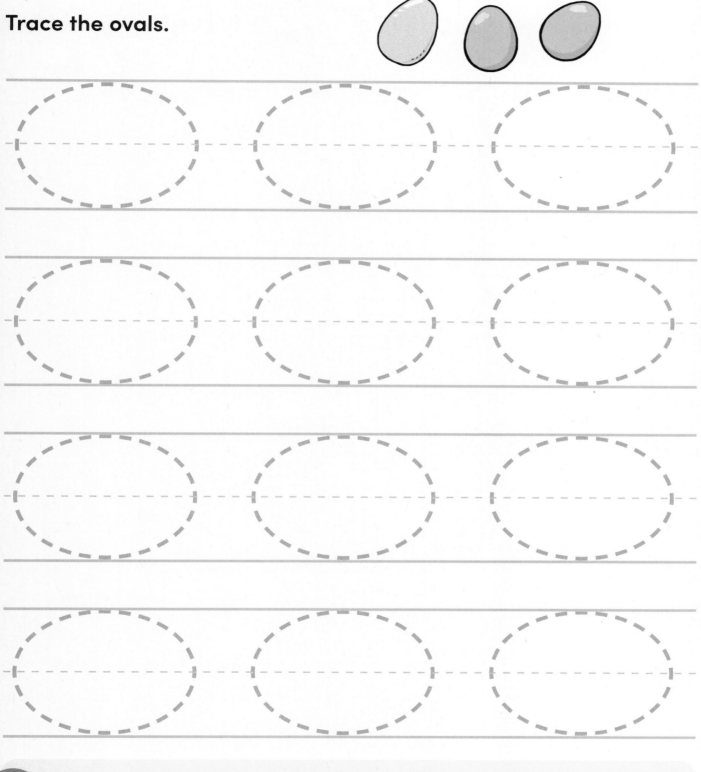

 Can you and your toddler find more oval shapes in your home or neighborhood?

Trace the hexagons.

 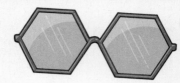

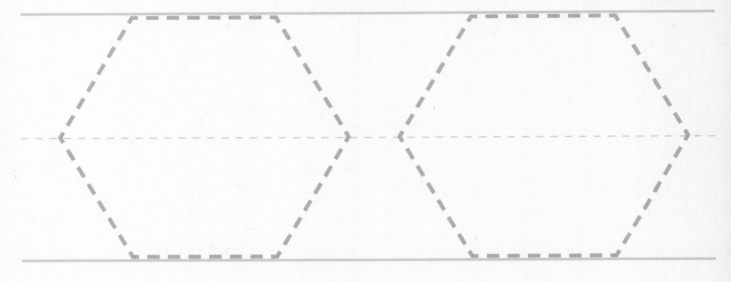

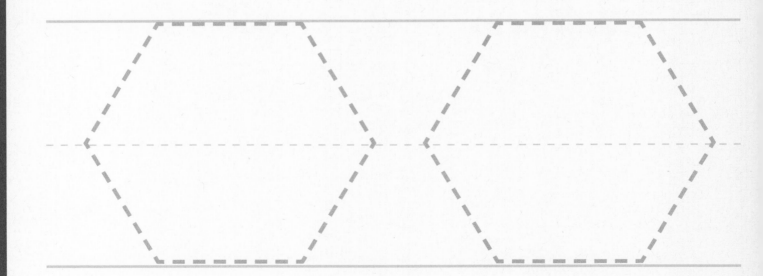

Can you and your toddler find more hexagon shapes in your home or neighborhood?

Trace the stars.

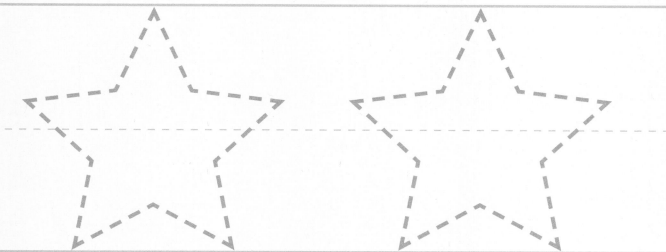

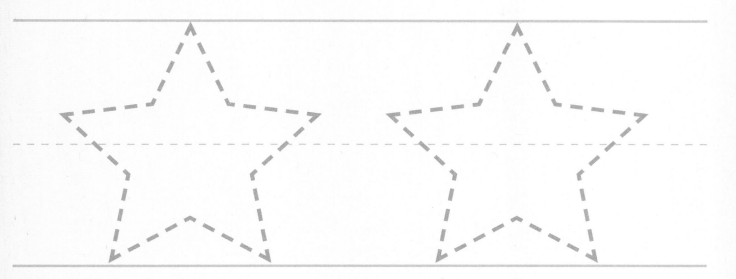

 Can you and your toddler find more star shapes in your home or neighborhood?

Trace the hearts.

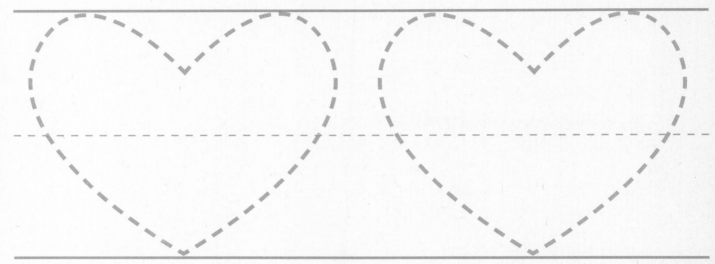

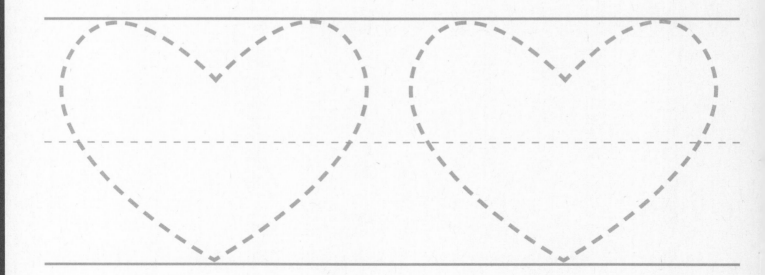

 Can you and your toddler find more heart shapes in your home or neighborhood?

Trace the crescents.

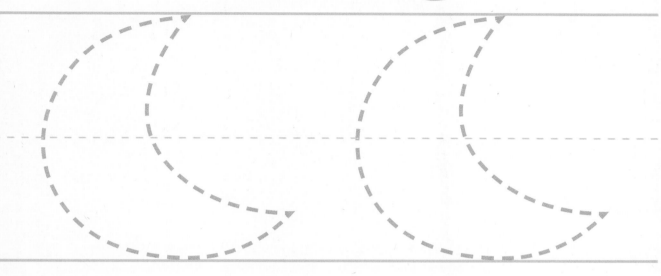

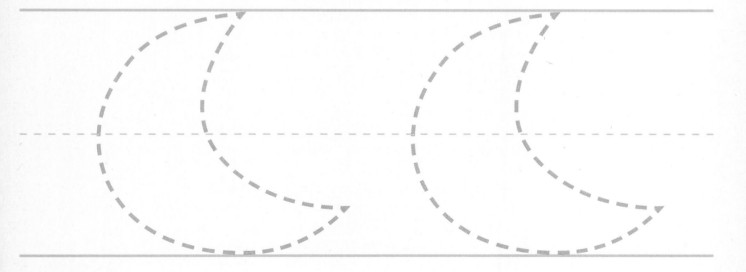

 Can you and your toddler find more crescent shapes in your home or neighborhood?

MORE ALPHABET

★ This section will continue to develop your toddler's ability to identify letters and begin to understand their unique sounds. Read the directions aloud. Then invite him or her to trace the featured letter and color the companion pictures.

★ Point to the three items that begin with the featured letter, such as *apple, airplane*, and *alligator*. Read them aloud slowly and clearly several times. Then invited your toddler to chime in and/or identify them.

★ Follow up the session with the starred EXTRA activity at the bottom of the page. This will help build your toddler's listening and speaking skills.

★ To reinforce learning, work with your toddler to cut out images from magazines or computer printouts that begin with the featured letter—such as *A*. Then paste them onto paper to create colorful letter collages.

SUPPLIES: crayons or washable markers

Trace the letter A. Then color the things that begin with A.

Alligator

Airplane

Apple

Point to each item and say its name. Then invite your toddler to do the same with or without your help.

Trace the letter B. Then color the things that begin with B.

Bike

Boy

Bear

 Point to each item and say its name. Then invite your toddler to do the same with or without your help.

Trace the letter C. Then color the things that begin with C.

Castle

Cat

Carrot

 Point to each item and say its name. Then invite your toddler to do the same with or without your help.

Trace the letter D. Then color the things that begin with D.

Dog

Door

Dinosaur

 Point to each item and say its name. Then invite your toddler to do the same with or without your help.

Trace the letter E. Then color the things that begin with E.

Elephant

Elf

Eyes

 Point to each item and say its name. Then invite your toddler to do the same with or without your help.

Trace the letter F. Then color the things that begin with F.

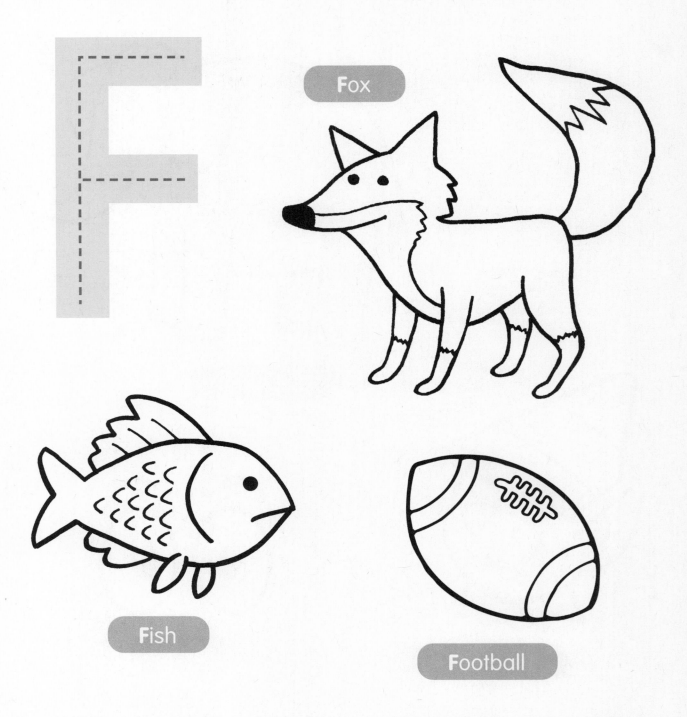

Fox

Fish

Football

 Point to each item and say its name. Then invite your toddler to do the same with or without your help.

Trace the letter G. Then color the things that begin with G.

Gorilla

Girl

Guitar

 Point to each item and say its name. Then invite your toddler to do the same with or without your help.

Trace the letter H. Then color the things that begin with H.

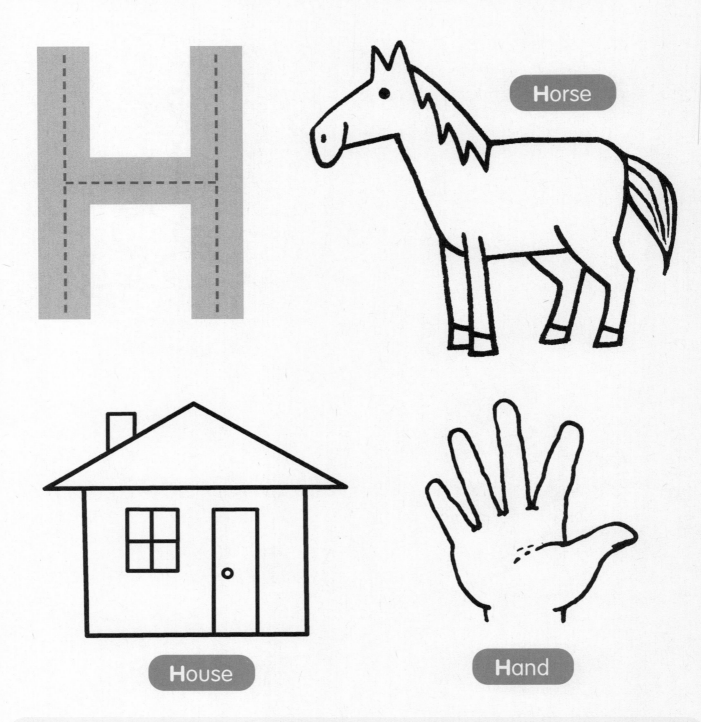

Horse

House

Hand

 Point to each item and say its name. Then invite your toddler to do the same with or without your help.

Trace the letter I. Then color the things that begin with I.

Iguana

Iron

Ice

 Point to each item and say its name. Then invite your toddler to do the same with or without your help.

Trace the letter J. Then color the things that begin with J.

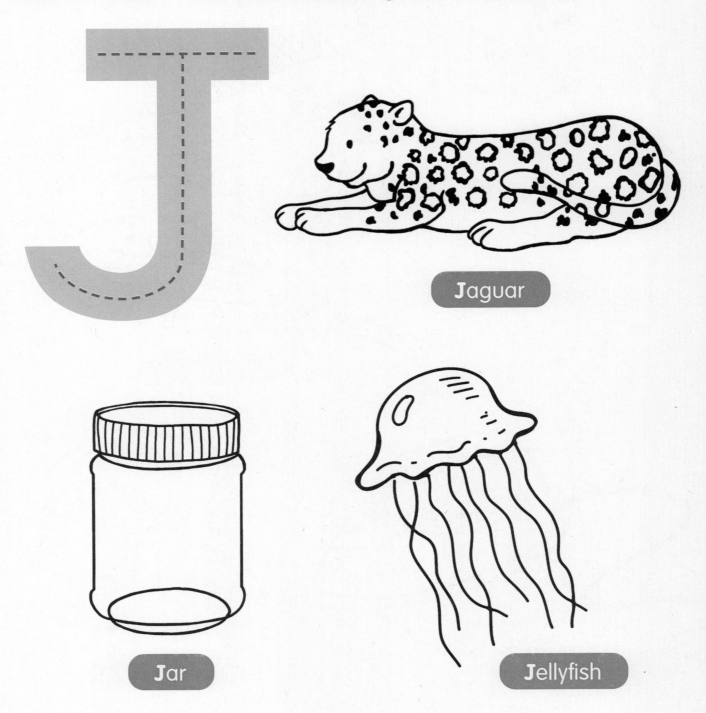

Jaguar

Jar

Jellyfish

Point to each item and say its name. Then invite your toddler to do the same with or without your help.

Trace the letter K. Then color the things that begin with K.

Keys

King

Ketchup

Point to each item and say its name. Then invite your toddler to do the same with or without your help.

Trace the letter L. Then color the things that begin with L.

Lion

Lamp

Ladder

 Point to each item and say its name. Then invite your toddler to do the same with or without your help.

Trace the letter M. Then color the things that begin with M.

Mouse

Mug

Monkey

 Point to each item and say its name. Then invite your toddler to do the same with or without your help.

Trace the letter N. Then color the things that begin with N.

Nest

Nine

Nail

Point to each item and say its name. Then invite your toddler to do the same with or without your help.

Trace the letter O. Then color the things that begin with O.

Owl

Octopus

Oven

 Point to each item and say its name. Then invite your toddler to do the same with or without your help.

Trace the letter P. Then color the things that begin with P.

Pig

Purse

Pencil

 Point to each item and say its name. Then invite your toddler to do the same with or without your help.

Trace the letter Q. Then color the things that begin with Q.

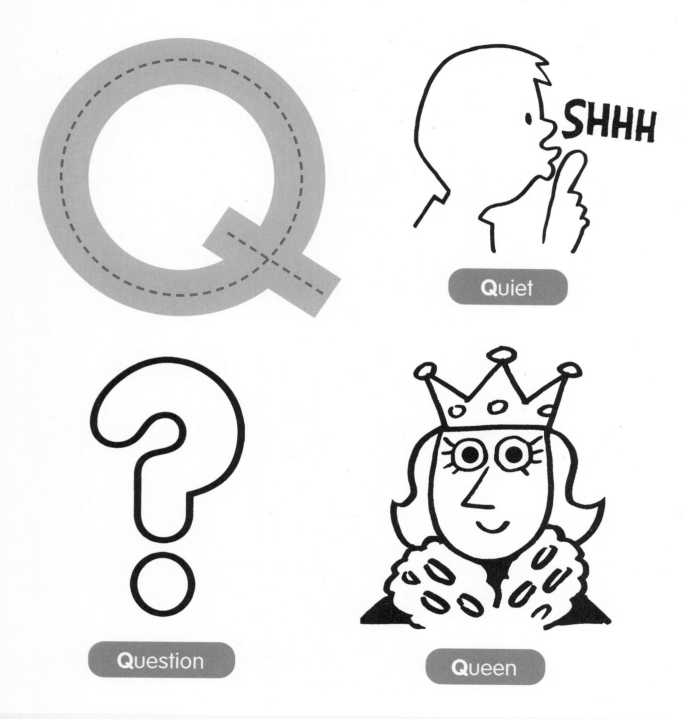

Quiet

Question

Queen

Point to each item and say its name. Then invite your toddler to do the same with or without your help.

Trace the letter R. Then color the things that begin with R.

Rainbow

Rabbit

Rocket

 Point to each item and say its name. Then invite your toddler to do the same with or without your help.

Trace the letter S. Then color the things that begin with S.

Socks

Seal

Sun

 Point to each item and say its name. Then invite your toddler to do the same with or without your help.

Trace the letter T. Then color the things that begin with T.

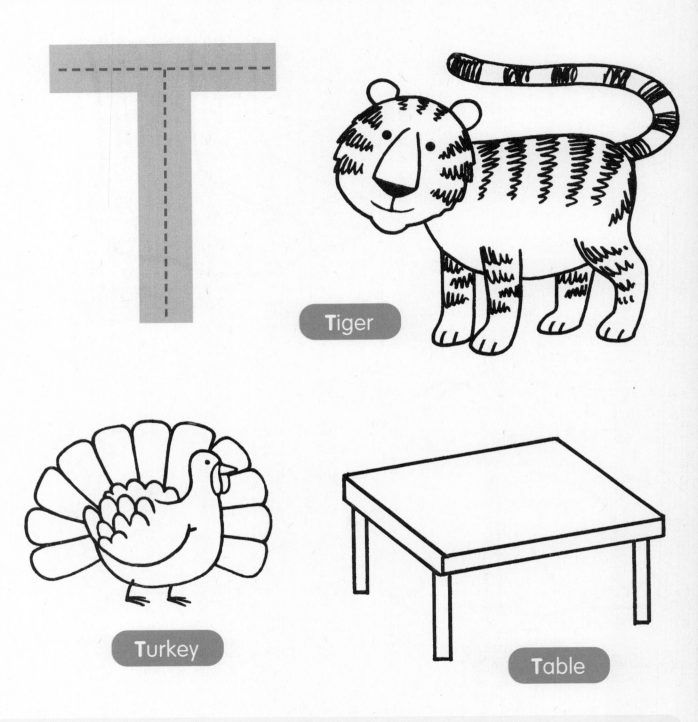

Tiger

Turkey

Table

 Point to each item and say its name. Then invite your toddler to do the same with or without your help.

Trace the letter U. Then color the things that begin with U.

Unicorn

Umbrella

Up

 Point to each item and say its name. Then invite your toddler to do the same with or without your help.

Trace the letter V. Then color the things that begin with V.

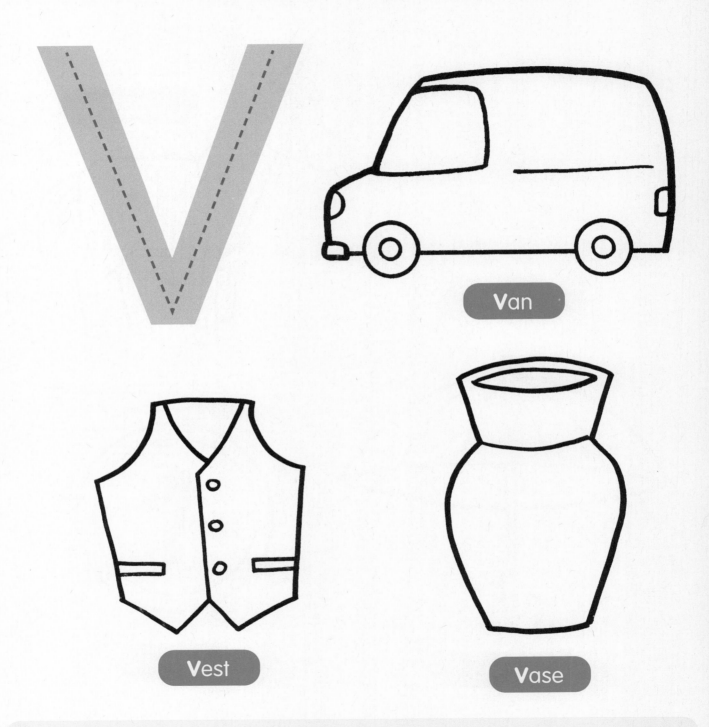

Van

Vest

Vase

 Point to each item and say its name. Then invite your toddler to do the same with or without your help.

Trace the letter W. Then color the things that begin with W.

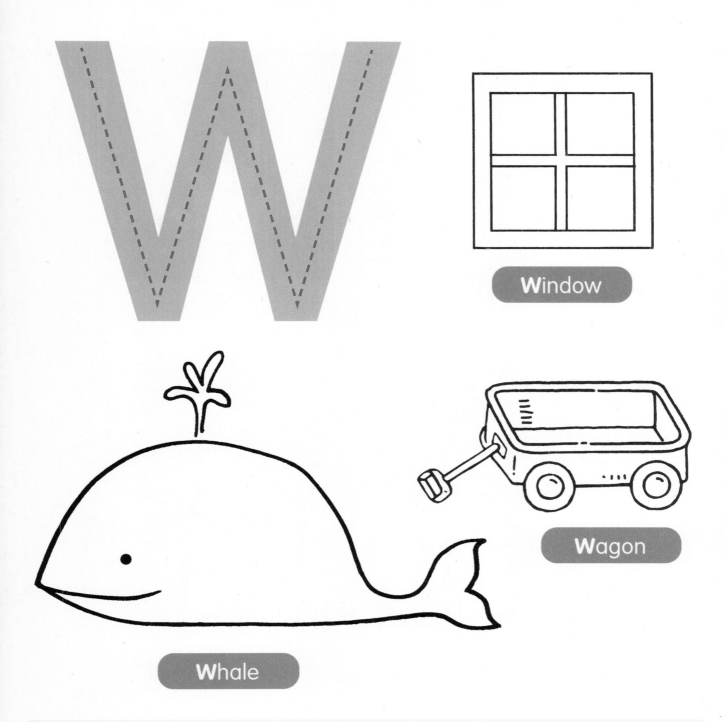

Window

Wagon

Whale

⭐ Point to each item and say its name. Then invite your toddler to do the same with or without your help.

Trace the letter X. Then color the things that begin or end with X.

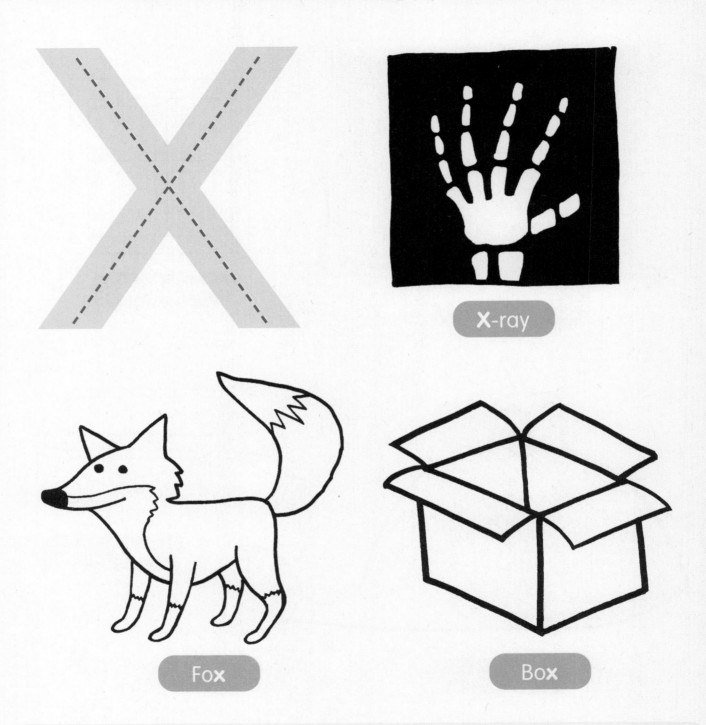

X-ray

Fox

Box

 Point to each item and say its name. Then invite your toddler to do the same with or without your help.

Trace the letter Y. Then color the things that begin with Y.

Yak

Yarn

Yell

Point to each item and say its name. Then invite your toddler to do the same with or without your help.

Trace the letter Z. Then color the things that begin with Z.

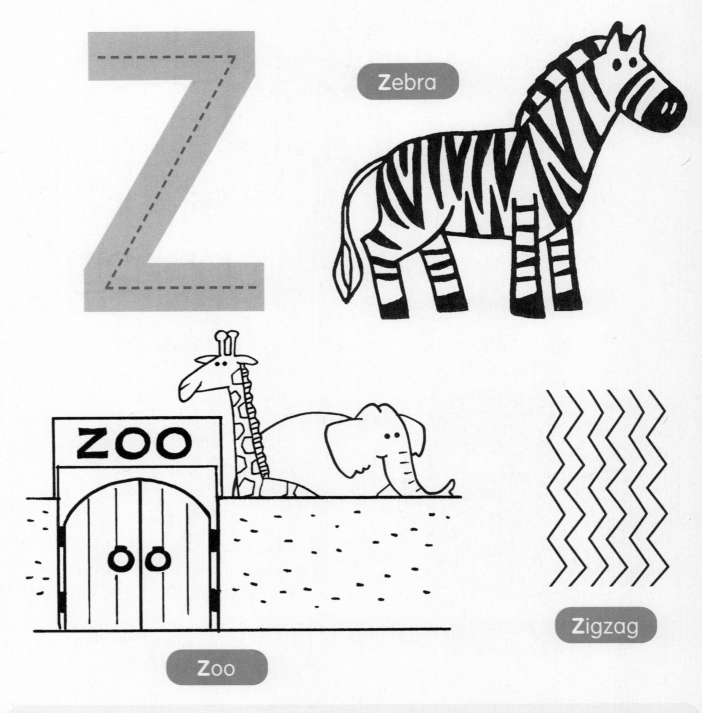

Zebra

ZOO

Zoo

Zigzag

 Point to each item and say its name. Then invite your toddler to do the same with or without your help.

MORE NUMBERS

★ This section will continue to develop your toddler's ability to identify numbers and grasp simple quantities. Read the directions aloud. Then invite him or her to trace the featured number and color the related item or items.

★ Along with your toddler, count the number of items in the picture such as *one truck, two candles, or three flowers.*

★ Follow up the session with the starred EXTRA activity at the bottom of the page. This will help build your toddler's listening and speaking skills.

★ To reinforce learning, count items in your home with your toddler such as *one teddy bear, two shoes, or three books.*

SUPPLIES: crayons or washable markers

Trace the number 1. Then color the 1 truck.

 Point to the number, say its name, and count the truck. Then invite your toddler to do the same with or without your help.

Trace the number 2. Then color the 2 candles.

 Point to the number, say its name, and count the candles. Then invite your toddler to do the same with or without your help.

Trace the number 3. Then color the 3 flowers.

 Point to the number, say its name, and count the flowers. Then invite your toddler to do the same with or without your help.

Trace the number 4. Then color the 4 scoops.

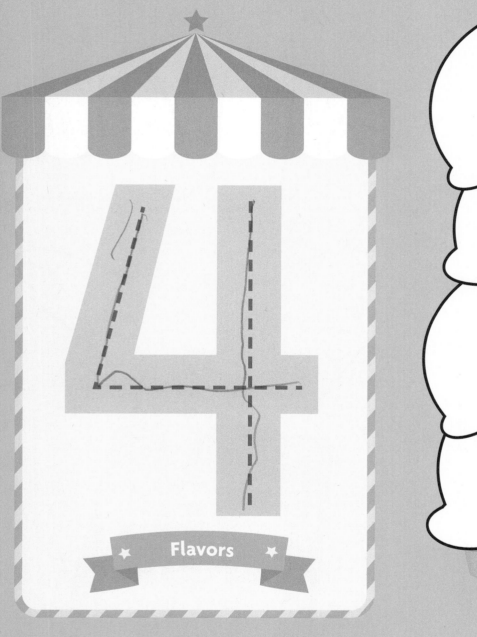

Flavors

 Point to the number, say its name, and count the scoops. Then invite your toddler to do the same with or without your help.

Trace the number 5. Then color the 5 fingers.

 Point to the number, say its name, and count the fingers. Then invite your toddler to do the same with or without your help.

Trace the number 6. Then color the 6 owls.

 Point to the number, say its name, and count the owls. Then invite your toddler to do the same with or without your help.

© Scholastic Inc.

Trace the number 7. Then color the 7 smiley faces.

 Point to the number, say its name, and count the smiley faces. Then invite your toddler to do the same with or without your help.

Trace the number 8. Then color the 8 octopus arms.

 Point to the number, say its name, and count the octopus arms. Then invite your toddler to do the same with or without your help.

Trace the number 9. Then color the 9 balloons.

 Point to the number, say its name, and count the balloons. Then invite your toddler to do the same with or without your help.

Trace the number 10. Then color the 10 bees.

 Point to the number, say its name, and count the bees. Then invite your toddler to do the same with or without your help.

MORE COLORS

★ This section will continue to develop your toddler's ability to recognize and name colors. Read the directions aloud. Invite your child to trace a circle around the requested item—such as a little red bug—and then color the large version of that item the same color.

★ Point to the featured item on the page—such as a bug—and invite your toddler to tell you about it. Augment their knowledge with age-appropriate facts, such as *bugs are little, they can crawl, they have six legs*, etc.

★ Follow up the session with the starred EXTRA activity at the bottom of the page. This will help build your toddler's listening and speaking skills.

★ To reinforce learning, place two to four items of different colors on a table, one of which is red. Then challenge your toddler to "grab the red one for me." Repeat the exercise to focus on other colors.

SUPPLIES: crayons or washable markers

Circle the little red bug. Then color the big bug red.

 Challenge your toddler to name other things that are red.

Circle the little blue bird. Then color the big bird blue.

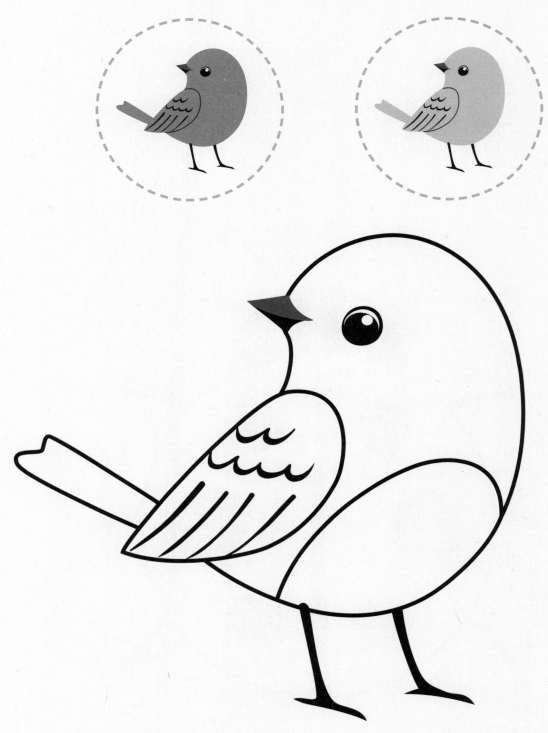

 Challenge your toddler to name other things that are blue.

Circle the little yellow car. Then color the big car yellow.

 Challenge your toddler to name other things that are yellow.

Circle the little green fish. Then color the big fish green.

 Challenge your toddler to name other things that are green.

Circle the little orange butterfly. Then color the big butterfly orange.

 Challenge your toddler to name other things that are orange.

Circle the little pink flower. Then color the big flower pink.

 Challenge your toddler to name other things that are pink.

Circle the little purple ball. Then color the big ball purple.

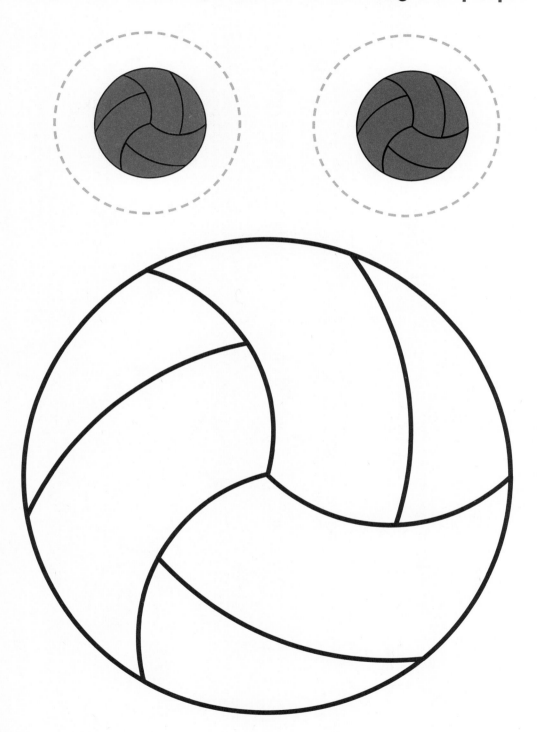

 Challenge your toddler to name other things that are purple.

Circle the little **brown** teddy bear. Then color the big teddy bear brown.

 Challenge your toddler to name other things that are brown.

Circle the little white ghost. Then color the big ghost white.

 Challenge your toddler to name other things that are white.

Circle the little **black** bat. Then color the big bat **black**.

 Challenge your toddler to name other things that are black.

Circle the little gray mouse. Then color the big mouse gray.

  Challenge your toddler to name other things that are gray.

Circle the little **rainbow** umbrella. Then color the big umbrella **rainbow** colors.

 Challenge your toddler to name other things that are lots of colors.

MORE SHAPES

★ This section will continue to develop your toddler's ability to recognize and name shapes. Read the directions aloud. Then invite him or her to trace a circle around the requested item—such as a square gift box—and then color the big version of that same item.

★ Point to the item in the picture—such as a square gift box—and invite your toddler to tell you about it. Can they think of something else that is the same shape?

★ Follow up the session with the starred EXTRA activity at the bottom of the page. This will help build your toddler's listening and speaking skills.

★ To reinforce learning, place two to four items of different shapes on a table, one of which is a square. Then challenge your toddler to "grab the square for me." Repeat the exercise to focus on other shapes.

SUPPLIES: crayons or washable markers

Circle the little circle-shape face. Then color the big one.

 Challenge your toddler to name other things that are a circle.

Circle the little square donut. Then color the big one.

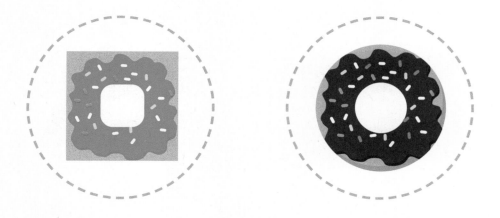

 Challenge your toddler to name other things that are a square.

Circle the little triangle-shape home. Then color the big one.

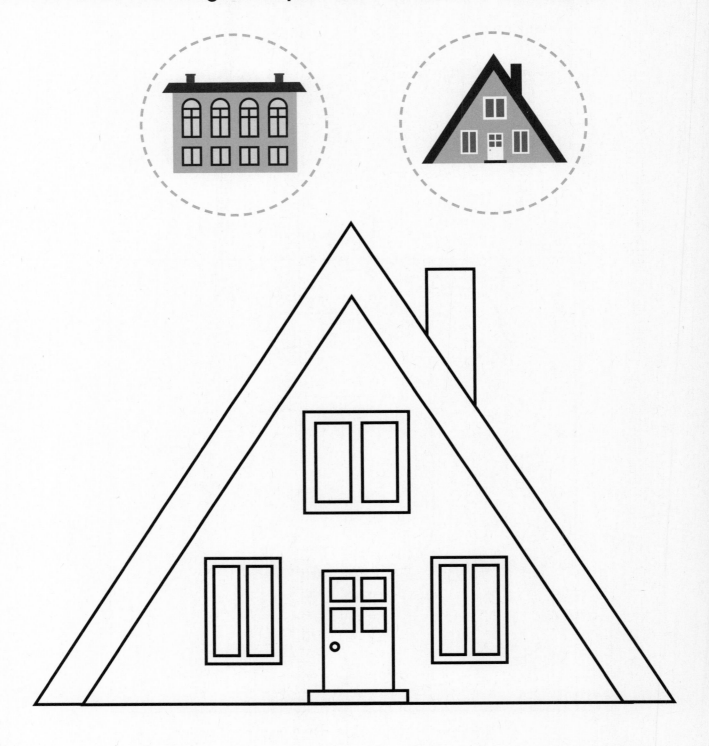

 Challenge your toddler to name other things that are a triangle.

Circle the little rectangle-shape window. Then color the big one.

 Challenge your toddler to name other things that are a rectangle.

Circle the little diamond-shape kite. Then color the big one.

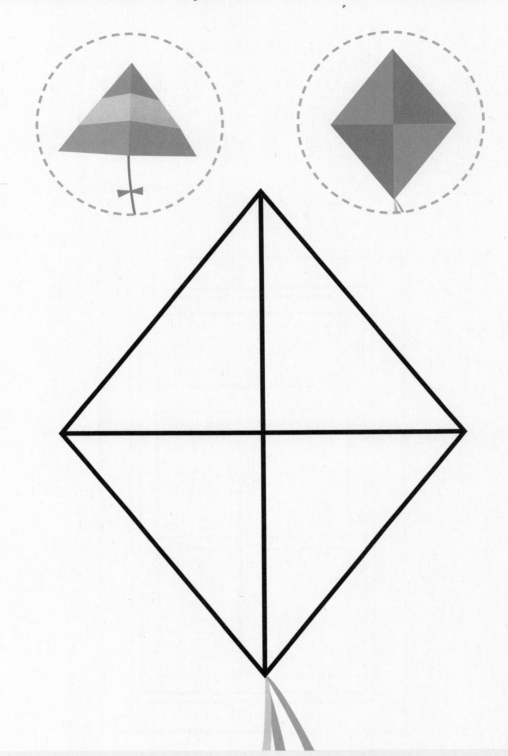

 Challenge your toddler to name other things that are a diamond.

Circle the little oval clock. Then color the big one.

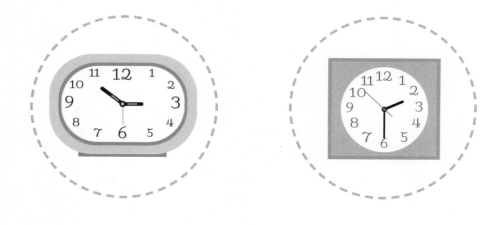

Challenge your toddler to name other things that are an oval.

Circle the little hexagon-shape monster. Then color the big one.

 Challenge your toddler to name other things that are a hexagon.

Circle the little star-shape sea creature. Then color the big one.

 Challenge your toddler to name other things that are a star.

Circle the heart-shape lollipop. Then color the big one.

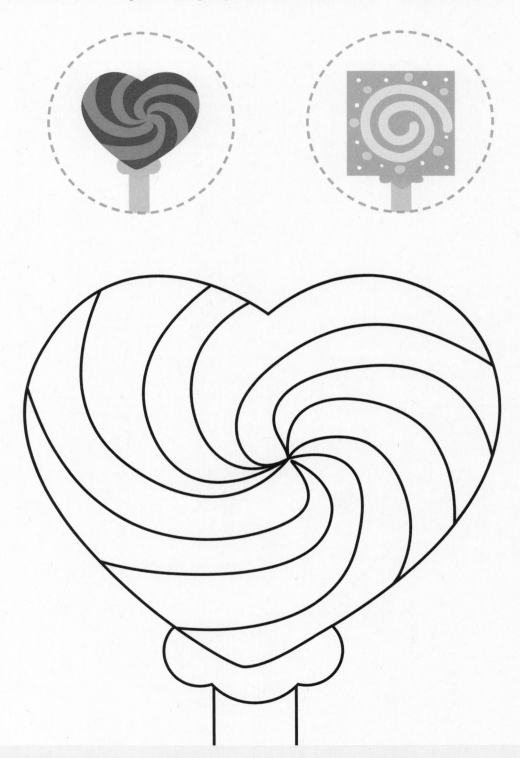

 Challenge your toddler to name other things that are a heart.

Circle the crescent-shape moon. Then color the big one.

 Challenge your toddler to name other things that are a crescent.

MORE CUTTING & PASTING

★ This section will continue to develop your toddler's ability to cut and paste. Read the directions aloud. Then invite him or her to cut and paste shapes to complete each picture. **Always supervise children when using scissors.**

★ If your toddler is too young to cut out a shape effectively, feel free to guide his or her hand when using the scissors. Or, do the cutting yourself. The gluing, too, can be done with or without your help. Cutting and pasting are skills that take time and practice, so be patient.

★ Follow up the session with the starred EXTRA activity at the bottom of the page. This will help build your toddler's listening and speaking skills.

★ To reinforce learning, work with your toddler to cut out images of beloved items—such as a truck—from magazines or computer printouts. Then paste them onto paper to create a colorful "Favorite Things" collage.

SUPPLIES: safety scissors and nontoxic glue stick

Cut out the pepperonis. Paste them on the pizza.

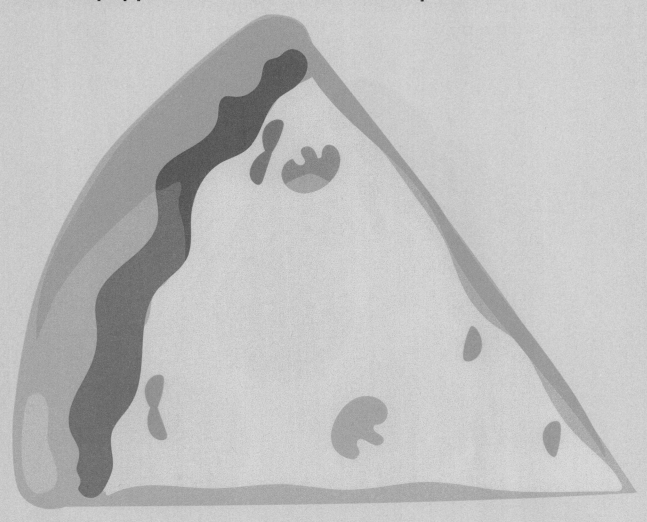

 Talk with your children about his or her favorite foods.

Talk with your toddler about pizza toppings. Discuss silly things you could put on a pizza.

Cut out the windows. Then paste them on the house.

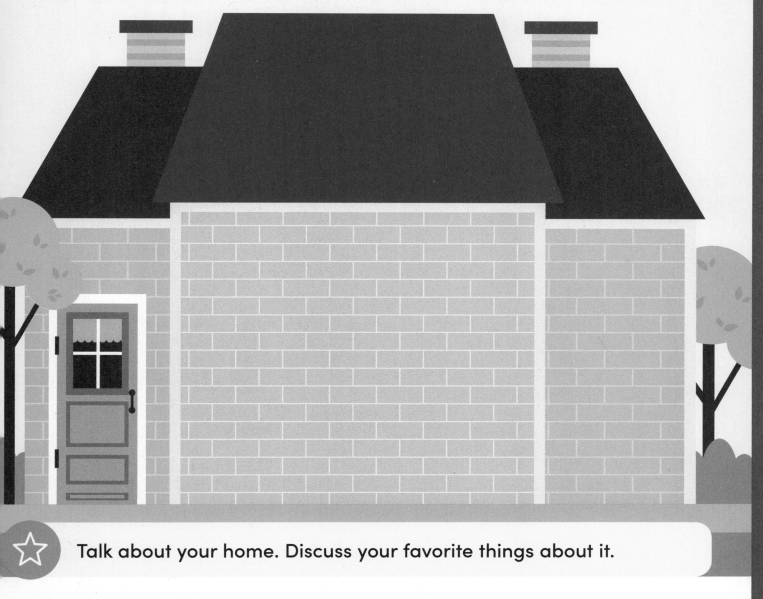

⭐ Talk about your home. Discuss your favorite things about it.

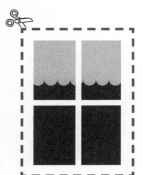 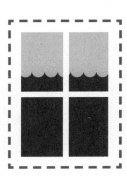 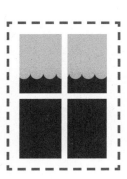 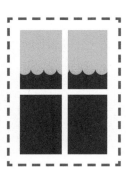

Look out your nearest window with your toddler. What can he/she see?

Cut out the sailboats. Then paste them on the lake.

 Talk with your toddler about boats. Where do boats go?

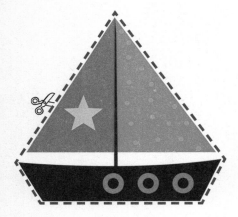  

Explain that boats go in the water. Where do cars go? Planes?

Cut out the books. Then paste them on the shelves.

 Talk with your toddler about books. What are his/her favorite books?

Snuggle with your toddler in a cozy spot. Then read a favorite book.

Cut out the footballs. Then paste them on the field.

Talk with your toddler about footballs. What can you do with them?

People catch, throw, and kick footballs. Demonstrate each action and invite your toddler to try.

Cut out the kites. Then paste them in the sky.

 Talk with your toddler about kites. Where do they fly?

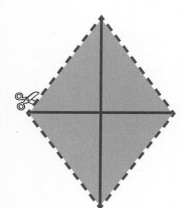
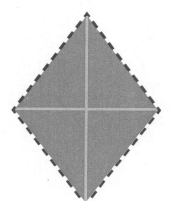
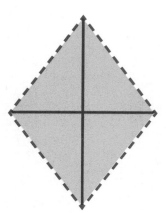

People fly kites in the sky. What else can fly in the sky?

Cut out the raindrops. Then paste them in the sky.

 Talk with your toddler about rain. Is is wet or dry?

What are some fun things to do on a rainy day? Discuss them.

Cut out the leaves. Then paste them on the branches.

 ⭐ Talk with your toddler about leaves. Where do leaves "live"?

Take a walk with your toddler and collect leaves. Then talk about them.

Cut out the hearts. Then paste them in the jar.

 Talk to your toddler about hearts. Explain they mean "I love you!"

Who would your toddler like to share his/her candy hearts with?

YOU ARE SWEET!

I MISS YOU!

I LOVE YOU!

MORE BASIC CONCEPTS

⭐ This section will reinforce your toddler's understanding of basic concepts. Read the directions aloud. Then invite him or her to color the items on the page as directed.

⭐ If your toddler struggles to understand the basic concept being presented—such as happy or sad—point to each item and say "happy" or "sad." You can also demonstrate by smiling or frowning, inviting your child to do the same.

⭐ Follow up the session with the starred EXTRA activity at the bottom of the page. This will help build your toddler's listening and speaking skills.

⭐ To reinforce learning, point out opposites in books and on TV shows, such as an animal that is short, like a turtle, or an animal that is tall, like a giraffe.

SUPPLIES: crayons or washable markers

Color the fish that is big  pink.
Color fish that is small purple.

Talk about big and small animals that live in the ocean.

Color the bug that is long blue.

Color the bug that is short red.

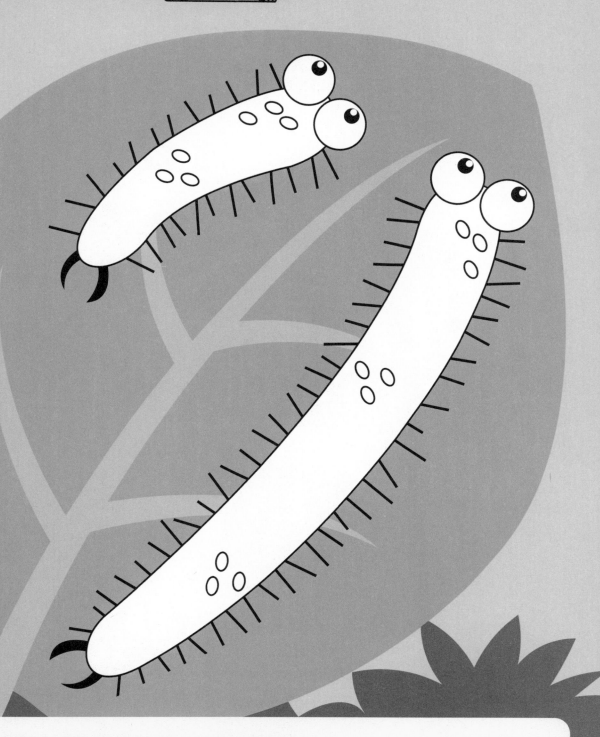

 Invite your toddler to pretend to be a bug.

Color the frog that is up  green.

Color the frog that is down yellow.

Invite your toddler to pretend to be a frog.

Color the building that is tall ▣ red.
Color the building that is short ▣ orange.

Ask your toddler, "Which building would a lot of people fit inside?"

Color the bat that is inside black.
Color the bat that is outside gray.

 Invite your toddler to pretend to be a bat.

Color the dinosaur that is happy orange.
Color the dinosaur that is sad yellow.

 Invite your toddler to pretend to be a dinosaur.

Color the teddy bear that is big  brown.
Color the teddy bear that is small purple.

 Does your toddler have a favorite stuffed toy? Talk about it.

Color the plane that is up gray.

Color the plane that is down white.

 Invite your toddler to pretend to be a plane.

Color the boat that is long green.
Color the boat that is short yellow.

 Boats can float on water. Talk with your toddler about things that can float in a bath tub.

Color the flower that is tall  pink.
Color the flower that is short purple.

⭐ Visit a garden and talk about flowers.

Color the bunny that is inside  brown.
Color the bunny that is outside white.

Invite your toddler to pretend to be a bunny.

Color the butterfly that is happy red.
Color the butterfly that is sad blue.

 Invite your toddler to pretend to be a butterfly.

MORE MATCHING

★ This section will reinforce your toddler's understanding of one-to-one correspondence. Read the directions aloud and name each pictured item. Then invite your child to draw lines to make matches. **Note:** A dashed line is provided for the first match.

★ If your toddler struggles to draw straight lines, feel free to guide his or her hand.

★ Follow up the session with the starred EXTRA activity at the bottom of the page. This will help build your toddler's listening and speaking skills.

★ To reinforce learning, play a game in which you place three items on a table, one of which is different from the others—such as one ball and two books. Then challenge your toddler to tell you which item is different.

SUPPLIES: crayons or washable markers

Draw lines to match the letters.

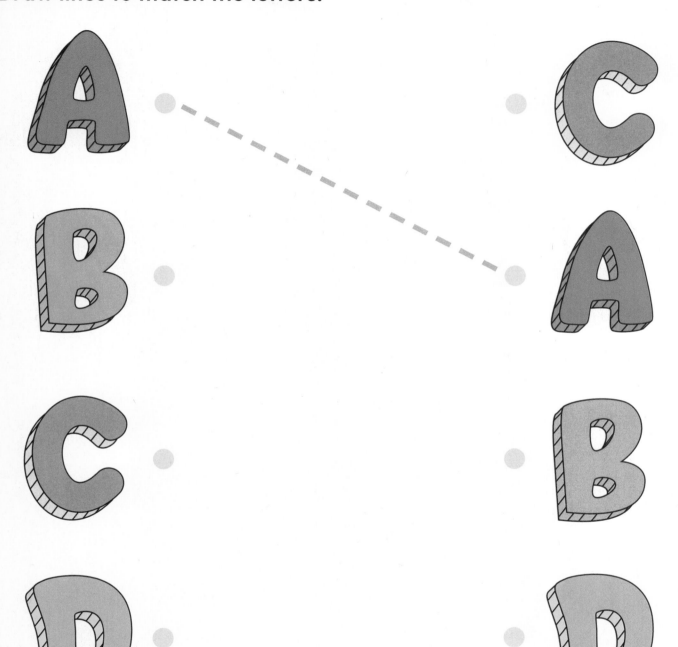

 Challenge your toddler to name these letters. Can he/she think of more letters?

Draw lines to match the numbers.

1

2

2

4

3

1

4

3

Challenge your toddler to name these numbers. Can he/she think of more numbers?

Draw lines to match the colors.

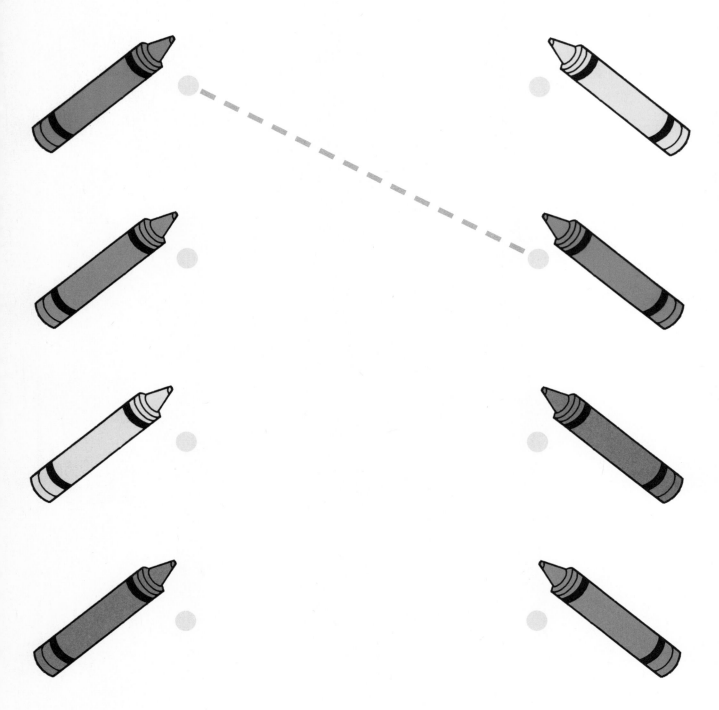

 Challenge your toddler to name these colors. Can he/she think of more colors?

Draw lines to match the shapes.

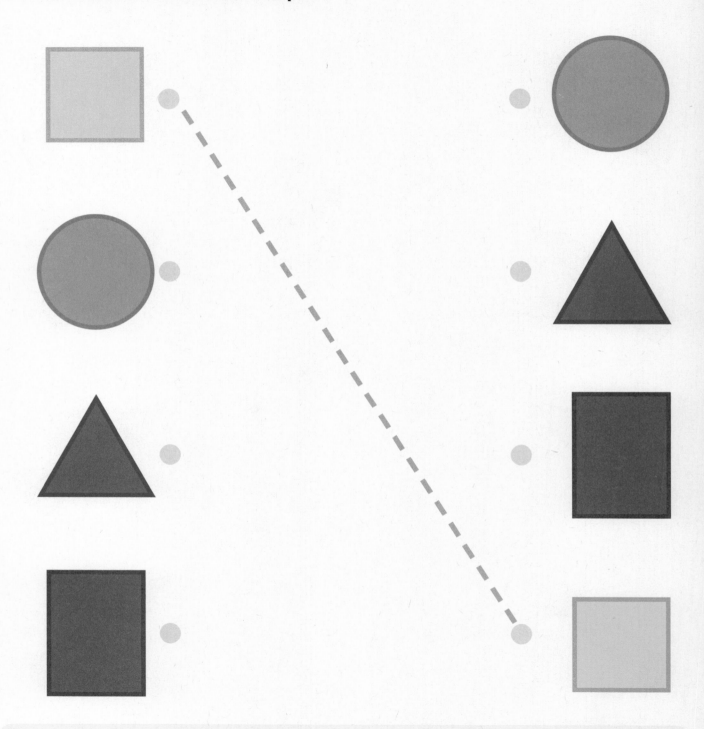

 Challenge your toddler to name these shapes. Can he/she think of more shapes?

Draw lines to match the faces.

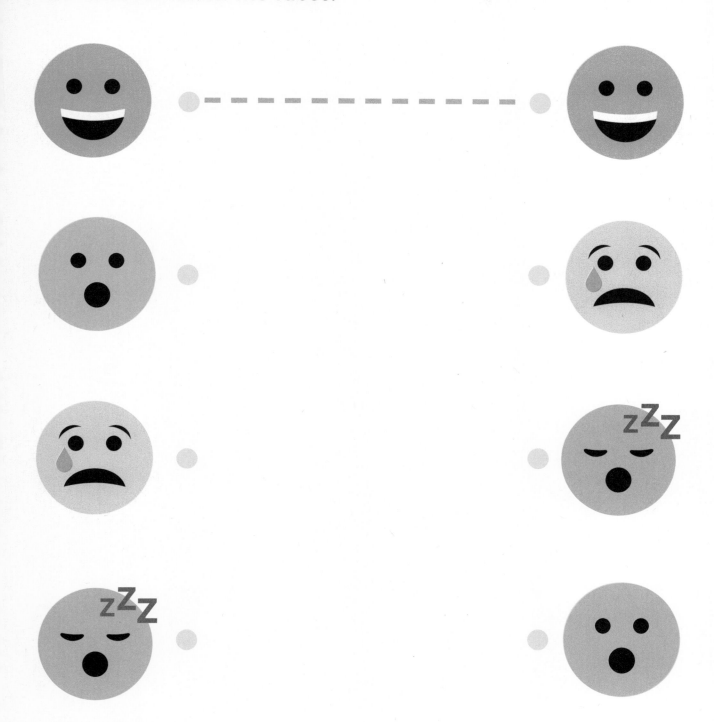

 Challenge your toddler to name these feelings. Can he/she think of more feelings?

Draw lines to match the monsters.

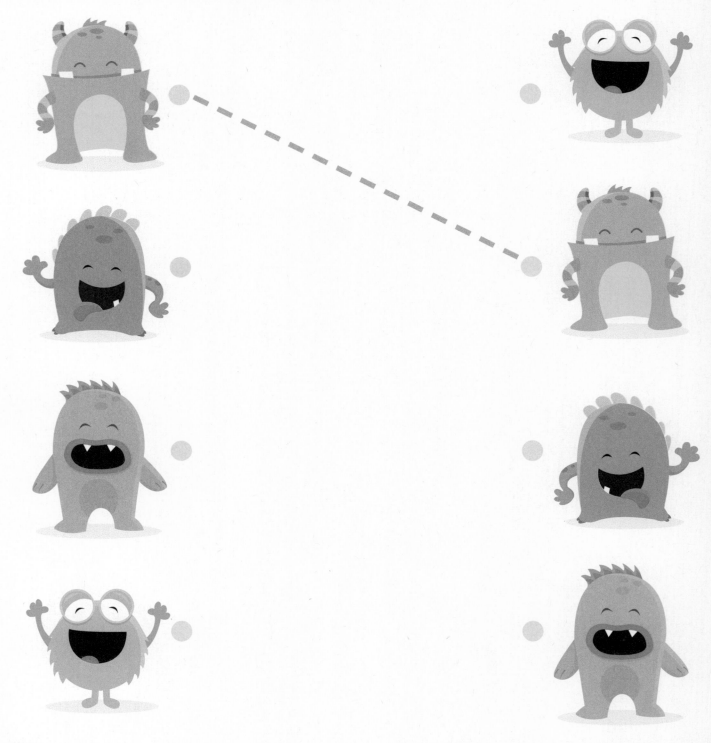

 Challenge your toddler to move like a monster.

Draw lines to match the superheroes.

 Challenge your toddler to move like a superhero.

Draw lines to match the dinosaurs.

 Challenge your toddler to move like a dinosaur.

Draw lines to match the fish.

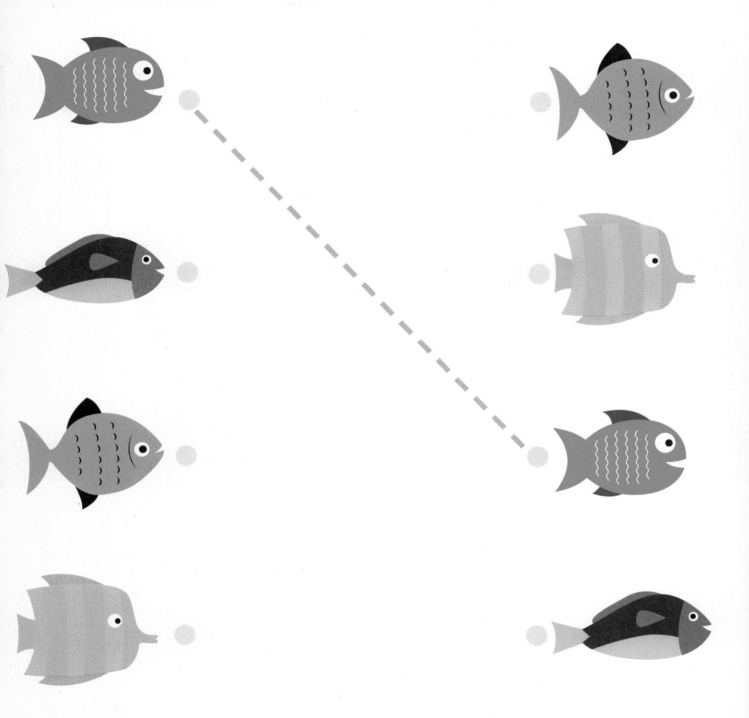

 Challenge your toddler to move like a fish.

Draw lines to match the butterflies.

 Challenge your toddler to move like a butterfly.

Draw lines to match the dogs.

 Challenge your toddler to move like a dog.

MORE SORTING

★ This section will reinforce your toddler's ability to sort, cut, and paste. Read the directions. Then, invite him or her to cut out the items at the bottom of the page and paste each with the correct group. **Always supervise children when using scissors.**

★ If your toddler is too young to cut effectively, feel free to guide his or her hand when using the safety scissors. The gluing, too, can be done with or without your help. Cutting and pasting are skills that take time and practice, so be patient and focus on fun.

★ Follow up the session with the starred EXTRA activities at the bottom and back of the page. This will help build your toddler's conversational and critical-thinking skills.

★ To reinforce learning, play a game in which you place three groups of objects on the floor—such as books, balls, and stuffed animals. Then give your child one or more of each item, challenging him/her to sort each into the right group. Repeat the activities with four groups of items.

SUPPLIES: crayons or washable markers, safety scissors, nontoxic glue stick

Cut out the letter and number at the bottom of the page. Then, paste each in the right group.

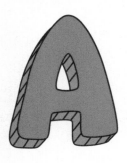 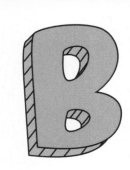

Find items in your home that begin with A, B, and C. Then, count items in groups of three.

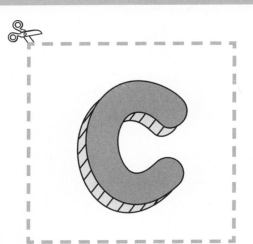

Point to each letter as you sing the alphabet song.

A B C D E F G

H I J K L M N

O P Q R S T U

V W X Y Z

Cut out the red and blue items at the bottom of the page. Then, paste each in the right group.

⭐ Point out items in your home or neighborhood that are red and blue.

Point to each T-shirt, challenging your toddler to tell you if it is red or blue.

Cut out the yellow and green items at the bottom of the page.
Then, paste each in the right group.

⭐ Point out items in your home or neighborhood that are yellow and green.

Point to each balloon, challenging your toddler to tell you if it is yellow or green.

Cut out the orange and purple items at the bottom of the page. Then, paste each in the right group.

⭐ Point out items in your home or neighborhood that are orange and purple.

Point to each party hat, challenging your toddler to tell you if it is orange or purple.

Cut out the shapes at the bottom of the page. Then, paste each in the right group.

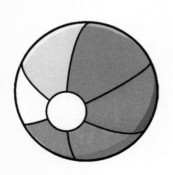 

⭐ Point out items in your home or neighborhood that are circles and squares.

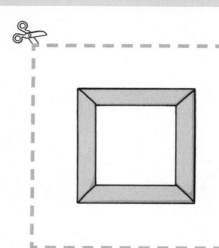 

Point to each window, challenging your toddler to tell you if it is a circle or a square.

Cut out the shapes at the bottom of the page. Then, paste each in the right group.

⭐ Point out items in your home or neighborhood that are triangles and rectangles.

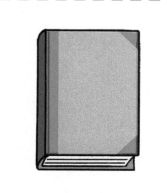

Point to each shape, challenging your toddler to tell you if it is a triangle or a rectangle.

Cut out the happy and sad faces at the bottom of the page. Then, paste each in the right group.

⭐ Talk to your toddler about things that make him/her happy and sad.

Point to each face, challenging your toddler to tell you if the child is happy or sad.

Cut out the sun and the moon at the bottom of the page. Then, paste each in the right group.

⭐ Talk to your toddler about things that you see during the day and at night.

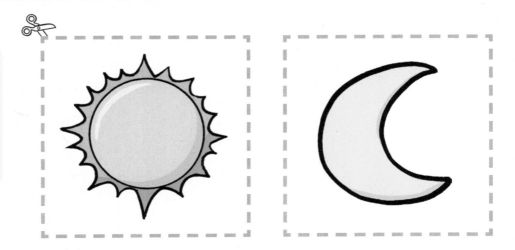

Which picture shows day and which picture shows night? Talk about what you see.

SCHOLASTIC SUCCESS WITH

EASY SONGS

★ Like nursery rhymes, classic songs are enjoyable and packed with learning. Not only do these "sticky" tunes boost oral language and vocabulary skills, they also set the stage for reading success because they help toddlers understand how words and language work.

★ Sing each song slowly, clearly, and with verve—encouraging your toddler to join in. There is no such thing as singing a song too many times. **Tip:** If you are unfamiliar with a particular song, find it online and give it a listen. You'll pick up the tune in no time.

★ Try the starred EXTRA activity at the bottom of the page, which enriches the song with a simple fingerplay, movement, or other activity.

★ To extend learning, complete the companion page. It provides an illustration to accompany the song as well as a skill-building activity.

SUPPLIES: crayons or washable markers

Sing the song with your toddler.

Pop Goes the Weasel

Round and round

the mulberry bush,

the monkey chased

the weasel.

The monkey thought

'twas all in fun—

POP goes the weasel.

 As you sing, walk in a circle—or around a Hula-Hoop—with your toddler. On *POP goes the weasel*, crouch down low, then jump up high.

Color the berries on the bush red.

Reread the rhyme, substituting two other animals for *monkey* and *weasel,* such as *kitty* and *bunny.* Or act it out with stuffed animals.

Sing the song with your toddler.

The Itsy Bitsy Spider

The itsy bitsy spider

crawled up the water spout.

Down came the rain,

and washed the spider out.

Out came the sun,

and dried up all the rain,

and the itsy bitsy spider

went up the spout again.

 On *crawled up the water spout*, run your fingers up your toddler's arm. On *washed the spider out*, run your fingers down his/her arm. On *out came the sun*, form a sun with your hands. On *went up the spout again*, run your fingers up your toddler's arm to his/her shoulder, then give up thumbs-up.

Color the spider green.

 Read an easy nonfiction book about spiders to your toddler.

Sing the song with your toddler.

Rain, Rain, Go Away

Rain, rain, go away.

Come again some other day.

Little _____ wants to play!
$\quad\quad\quad\quad$ toddler's name

Rain, rain, go away.

Sun, sun, you can stay.

You can chase the clouds away.

Little _____ wants to play!
$\quad\quad\quad\quad$ toddler's name

Sun, sun, you can stay.

For the first verse, wiggle your fingers downward to suggest falling rain. For the second verse, form a circle with your hands, moving them upward to suggest a rising sun. Challenge your toddler to do the same.

Draw more rain falling from the sky.

 Talk to your toddler about the many kinds of weather in the world, including sun, rain, snow, and wind.

Sing the song with your toddler.

Twinkle, Twinkle, Little Star

Twinkle, twinkle, little star,

how I wonder what you are!

Up above the world so high,

like a diamond in the sky.

Twinkle, twinkle, little star,

how I wonder what you are!

On *Twinkle, twinkle little star*, open and close your hands like twinkling stars. On *how I wonder*, point to your head as if you're thinking. On *up above the world*, reach skyward. On *like a diamond*, form a diamond shape with your two hands. Invite your toddler to copy your movements.

Trace the stars and color them yellow.

When it gets dark, look at the stars and talk about them with your toddler.

Sing the song with your toddler.

The Ants Go Marching

The ants go marching

one by one, hurrah, hurrah!

The ants go marching

one by one, hurrah, hurrah!

The ants go marching

one by one, the little one stops

to suck his thumb.

And they all go marching

down to the ground

to get out of the rain.

 As you sing, invite your toddler to pretend to be a marching ant.

Color the ants red.

⭐ Ants are amazing! Share an easy nonfiction book about them with your toddler.

Sing the song with your toddler.

The Wheels on the Bus

The wheels on the bus

go round and round,

round and round,

round and round.

The wheels on

the bus go round and round—

all through the town.

 Invite your toddler to pretend to be a bus and go "all through the town."

Color the school bus  yellow.

Talk to your child about other vehicles with wheels that go round and round, such as bikes, cars, and trucks.

Sing the song with your toddler.

Row, Row, Row Your Boat

Row, row, row your boat,

gently down the stream.

Merrily, merrily,

merrily, merrily—

life is but a dream.

 Give your toddler two paper-towel tubes to use as oars, inviting him/her to "row" as you sing.

Trace the waves on the ocean.

 Talk to your toddler about boats. Then, read a fiction or nonfiction book about them!

Sing the song with your toddler.

Ring Around the Rosie

Ring around the rosie,

a pocket full of posies—

Ashes! Ashes!

We all fall down!

Face your toddler and hold hands as you sing, turning in a clockwise circle. On *We all fall down*, joyfully drop to the ground. Repeat.

Color the roses on the bush  **red.**

 Invite family and friends—even stuffed animals!—to play Ring Around the Rosie with you and your toddler.

Sing the song with your toddler.

London Bridge

London Bridge is falling down,

falling down,

falling down.

London Bridge is falling down—

my fair lady.

Build it up with sticks and stones,

sticks and stones,

sticks and stones—

my fair lady.

 On *London Bridge is falling down*, flutter your fingers downward to suggest falling. On *Build it up with sticks and stones*, place a fist on top of a fist to suggest building. Invite your toddler to copy you.

Help fix the bridge by putting a on each of its broken parts.

Use blocks to help your toddler build a tower or simple bridge.

Sing the song with your toddler.

It's Raining, It's Pouring

It's raining, it's pouring,

the old man is snoring.

He went to bed and

bumped his head

and dreamt of cats

'til the morning.

 Change *cats* to another animal or item—such as *dogs* or *cake*—then sing the poem again.

Color the cats black **and** orange.

 Talk about sleep and dreams with your toddler.

Sing the song with your toddler.

Alphabet Song

A–B–C–D–E–F–G

H–I–J–K–LMNOP

Q–R–S

T–U–V

W and X

Y and Z.

Now we know our A–B–C's.

Let's all sing from A to Z!

 Invite your toddler to point to any letter. When he/she does, name something that begins with it, such as *tiger* for T.

Write your toddler's name on the line. Then help him/her circle all the letters in it.

My name

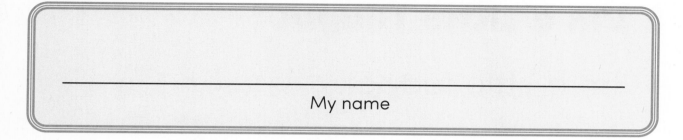

A B C D E F G

H I J K L M N

O P Q R S T U

V W X Y Z

 Talk to your toddler about the letters in his/her name—especially the one it begins with!

Sing the song with your toddler.

I'm a Little Teapot

I'm a little teapot,

short and stout.

Here is my handle,

here is my spout.

When I get all steamed up,

hear me shout.

Just tip me over,

and pour me out!

On *Here is my handle*, put your left hand on your hip. On *here is my spout*, stick out your right arm. On *tip me over and pour me out*, bend your body to the right as if pouring out tea. Invite your toddler to do the same.

Color the teapot green.

 Have a tea party with your toddler and his/her stuffed animals.

Sing the song with your toddler.

Six Little Ducks

Six little ducks went to play—

wibble wobble, wibble wobble

to and fro.

But the one little duck

with the feather on his back,

he led the others with a

quack, quack, quack.

Quack, quack, quack.

Quack, quack, quack.

 As you sing, invite your toddler to pretend to be a duck by waddling, flapping his/her arms, and quacking.

Count the ducks and color them yellow.

★ Challenge your toddler to find "the one little duck with the feather on his back." Then, go to a park and feed some ducks!

Sing the song with your toddler.

Mary Had a Little Lamb

Mary had a little lamb,

little lamb, little lamb.

Mary had a little lamb,

its fleece was white as snow.

And everywhere that Mary went,

Mary went, Mary went.

Everywhere that Mary went,

the lamb was sure to go.

Change *Mary* to the name of your toddler. Then, sing it again!

Trace the lamb's fur, then color it  white.

 Invite your toddler to pretend to be a lamb and say "Baaaah!"

Sing the song with your toddler.

If You're Happy and You Know It

If you're happy and you know it,

clap your hands. (CLAP, CLAP.)

If you're happy and you know it,

clap your hands. (CLAP, CLAP.)

If you're happy and you know it,

then your face will surely show it.

If you're happy and you know it,

clap your hands. (CLAP, CLAP.)

 Each time *clap your hands* is sung, invite your toddler to clap his/her hands twice. On *then your face will surely show it*, invite him/her to smile broadly.

Trace the smiles on the happy faces.

 Count the happy faces with your toddler. Then, talk about things that make him/her smile.

Sing the song with your toddler.

Old MacDonald

Old MacDonald had a farm,

E-I-E-I-O.

And on his farm, he had a cow,

E-I-E-I-O.

With a MOO, MOO here

and a MOO, MOO there.

Here a MOO, there a MOO,

everywhere a MOO, MOO!

Old Macdonald had a farm,

E-I-E-I-O.

Sing the song again, but replace "cow" and "MOO" with a new animal and sound, for example: *And on his farm he had a <u>horse</u>, E-I-E-I-O. With a "NEIGH, NEIGH" here and a "NEIGH, NEIGH" there.*

Trace the cow's spots and color them black.

 Visit a farm with your toddler and/or share a simple book about farms.

Sing the song with your toddler.

Rock-a-Bye Baby

Rock-a-bye, baby

in the treetop.

When the wind blows,

the cradle will rock.

When the bough breaks

the cradle will fall.

And Mommy will catch you—

cradle and all.

 As you sing, rock your toddler on your lap. Or invite your toddler to rock a doll or stuffed animal. NOTE: *Mommy* can be changed to *Daddy, Auntie,* etc.

Trace the leaves on the tree and color them green.

 Share baby pictures with your toddler. Discuss how he/she has changed and learned new things.

· SCHOLASTIC SUCCESS WITH ·

ALL ABOUT ME

★ Welcome to the ALL ABOUT ME booklet—starring your toddler! The activities in this section celebrate the things that make your little one unique.

★ Read the directions aloud and work together: You fill in the text while your toddler does the coloring. **Tip:** Take your time. Doing just a page or two in a sitting will make the completion of the booklet a thoughtful, joyful experience.

★ When the pages are complete, remove and staple them in order along the left-hand side. **Tip:** Place strips of clear tape over the top and bottom of the staples to protect little fingers.

★ Share the booklet with your toddler, modeling how to carefully turn the pages and take good care of a treasured item. Then, put the booklet in a safe place, revisiting it with your child as he or she grows. It's a keepsake you both can enjoy for a lifetime!

SUPPLIES: crayons or washable markers, stapler, tape

ALL ABOUT ME

Place a photo or drawing of your toddler here.

by the one and only

_____
name

CONTENTS

MY GREAT NAME

Write your toddler's name in the box and complete the sentences.
Then, invite him/her to color in the bubble letters.

I ♥ MY NAME...

_____
toddler's name

It begins with the letter _____ .
letter

It has _____ **letters in it.**
number

It is GREAT because _____
reason

_____ .

MY AWESOME AGE

Write your toddler's age on the line. Then, invite him/her to color in the right number of candles.

_____

age

MY FABULOUS FACE

Help your toddler draw his/her features on the face.
Then, complete the sentences.

I have _____ eyes.
color

I have _____ hair.
color

I have a big smile, too!

MY LOVED ONES

Write the names of your toddler's loved ones—
including **family**, **friends**, **and animals**—on the heart.
Then, invite **him/her** to color the border.

 # MY FIRST WORDS

Write your toddler's first words in the speech balloon.
Then, invite him/her to color the baby's face.

MY SUPERPOWERS

Write super things your toddler can do in the burst. Then, invite him/her to color the little superheroes.

MY FAVORITE FOOD

Write your toddler's favorite food on the line. Then, invite him/her to draw it on the plate with or without your help.

favorite food

MY FAVORITE BOOK

Write the name and author of your toddler's favorite book on the cover. Then, invite him/her to decorate it.

My favorite book is

_____
title

by _____
author

MY FAVORITE TOY

Write your toddler's favorite toy on the line. Then, help him/her draw or paste a picture of it in the toy box.

favorite toy

MY FAVORITE ANIMAL

Write your toddler's favorite animal on the line. Then, help him/her draw or paste a picture of that animal in the frame.

favorite animal

MY MOODS

Complete the page with your toddler. Then, invite him/her to color the faces.

I am happy when

_____

what makes toddler happy

_____

I am sad when

_____

what makes toddler sad

_____

MY BEST BUDDY

Complete the sentences with your toddler. Then, help him/her draw or paste a picture with a best buddy below.

My best buddy is _____.

special friend

We like to _____.

activity

MY TODDLER SONG

Fill in the blanks to create a special song about your toddler.
Sing it to the tune of "Happy Birthday!"

We love _____,
               name
we do!
We love _____,
               name
yahoo!

_____ loves _____
          name   something toddler loves

and _____, too!
        something toddler loves

BYE-BYE!

Write a fun fact about your amazing toddler.
Then, trace around his/her hand as if waving good-bye.

Here is one more thing you need to know about me...

_____

fact about your toddler

_____

Here is my hand waving
good-bye to you!